Table of Contents

How to Use This Book

This Premium Education Series workbook is designed to suit your teaching needs. Since every child learns at his or her own pace, this workbook can be used individually or as part of small group instruction. The activity pages can be used together with other educational materials and are easily applied to a variety of teaching approaches.

Contents
A detailed table of contents lists all the skills that are covered in the workbook.

Units
The workbook is divided into units of related skills. Numbered tabs allow you to quickly locate each unit. The skills within each unit are designed to be progressively more challenging.

Activity Pages
Each activity page is titled with the skill being practiced or reinforced. The activities and units in this workbook can be used in sequential order, or they can be used to accommodate and supplement any educational curriculum. In addition, the activity pages include simple instructions to encourage independent study, and they are printed in black and white so they can be easily reproduced. Plus, you can record the child's name and the date the activity was completed on each page to keep track of learning progress.

Practice Test
A comprehensive practice test helps prepare the child for standardized testing in a stress-free environment. Presented in the fill-in-the-circle format, this test includes skills covered on standardized tests.

Answer Key
The pages in the back of the workbook provide answers for each activity page as well as the practice test. These answer pages allow you to quickly check the child's work and provide immediate feedback on how he or she is progressing.

Addition Terms

Name_____ Date_____

Look at the chart. The **sum** of 3 is shown where the row for the **addend** 1 and the column for the **addend** 2 meet. You see that **1 + 2 = 3**.

Write the **sums** to finish the chart. Add the **addends** by row and column.

1.

+	0	1	2	3	4	5	6
0	0	1	2				
1	1	2	3				
2							
3							
4							
5							
6							

$$\begin{array}{r} 1 \leftarrow \textbf{addend} \\ +\ 2 \leftarrow \textbf{addend} \\ \hline 3 \leftarrow \textbf{sum} \end{array}$$

Write the missing **addend**.

2. $4 + \underline{} = 8$ $\underline{} + 3 = 5$ $6 + \underline{} = 12$ $\underline{} + 5 = 10$

3. $\underline{} + 6 = 6$ $2 + \underline{} = 8$ $\underline{} + 0 = 0$ $5 + \underline{} = 9$

Find the **sum**.

4.
$$\begin{array}{r} 4 \\ +\ 0 \\ \hline \end{array} \qquad \begin{array}{r} 5 \\ +\ 2 \\ \hline \end{array} \qquad \begin{array}{r} 1 \\ +\ 6 \\ \hline \end{array} \qquad \begin{array}{r} 4 \\ +\ 6 \\ \hline \end{array} \qquad \begin{array}{r} 6 \\ +\ 3 \\ \hline \end{array} \qquad \begin{array}{r} 2 \\ +\ 4 \\ \hline \end{array} \qquad \begin{array}{r} 3 \\ +\ 5 \\ \hline \end{array}$$

Addition Practice

Name_____ Date_____

Find the sum.

1. $3 + 4 =$ _____ $4 + 5 =$ _____ $4 + 2 =$ _____ $8 + 1 =$ _____

2. $5 + 3 =$ _____ $1 + 5 =$ _____ $0 + 9 =$ _____ $7 + 1 =$ _____

3. $8 + 0 =$ _____ $7 + 2 =$ _____ $2 + 0 =$ _____ $2 + 3 =$ _____

4. $1 + 2 =$ _____ $4 + 4 =$ _____ $4 + 1 =$ _____ $2 + 5 =$ _____

5.
$$
\begin{array}{r} 9 \\ + 0 \\ \hline \end{array} \quad
\begin{array}{r} 4 \\ + 3 \\ \hline \end{array} \quad
\begin{array}{r} 6 \\ + 2 \\ \hline \end{array} \quad
\begin{array}{r} 5 \\ + 1 \\ \hline \end{array} \quad
\begin{array}{r} 1 \\ + 6 \\ \hline \end{array} \quad
\begin{array}{r} 8 \\ + 8 \\ \hline \end{array} \quad
\begin{array}{r} 4 \\ + 9 \\ \hline \end{array}
$$

6.
$$
\begin{array}{r} 3 \\ + 6 \\ \hline \end{array} \quad
\begin{array}{r} 8 \\ + 7 \\ \hline \end{array} \quad
\begin{array}{r} 5 \\ + 7 \\ \hline \end{array} \quad
\begin{array}{r} 0 \\ + 3 \\ \hline \end{array} \quad
\begin{array}{r} 2 \\ + 7 \\ \hline \end{array} \quad
\begin{array}{r} 6 \\ + 7 \\ \hline \end{array} \quad
\begin{array}{r} 8 \\ + 6 \\ \hline \end{array}
$$

7.
$$
\begin{array}{r} 2 \\ + 2 \\ \hline \end{array} \quad
\begin{array}{r} 3 \\ + 3 \\ \hline \end{array} \quad
\begin{array}{r} 5 \\ + 9 \\ \hline \end{array} \quad
\begin{array}{r} 5 \\ + 2 \\ \hline \end{array} \quad
\begin{array}{r} 3 \\ + 6 \\ \hline \end{array} \quad
\begin{array}{r} 4 \\ + 8 \\ \hline \end{array} \quad
\begin{array}{r} 6 \\ + 5 \\ \hline \end{array}
$$

8.
$$
\begin{array}{r} 8 \\ + 3 \\ \hline \end{array} \quad
\begin{array}{r} 9 \\ + 6 \\ \hline \end{array} \quad
\begin{array}{r} 4 \\ + 7 \\ \hline \end{array} \quad
\begin{array}{r} 0 \\ + 4 \\ \hline \end{array} \quad
\begin{array}{r} 8 \\ + 9 \\ \hline \end{array} \quad
\begin{array}{r} 7 \\ + 7 \\ \hline \end{array} \quad
\begin{array}{r} 6 \\ + 6 \\ \hline \end{array}
$$

9.
$$
\begin{array}{r} 1 \\ + 7 \\ \hline \end{array} \quad
\begin{array}{r} 3 \\ + 5 \\ \hline \end{array} \quad
\begin{array}{r} 9 \\ + 4 \\ \hline \end{array} \quad
\begin{array}{r} 2 \\ + 5 \\ \hline \end{array} \quad
\begin{array}{r} 2 \\ + 1 \\ \hline \end{array} \quad
\begin{array}{r} 2 \\ + 8 \\ \hline \end{array} \quad
\begin{array}{r} 9 \\ + 9 \\ \hline \end{array}
$$

10.
$$
\begin{array}{r} 9 \\ + 7 \\ \hline \end{array} \quad
\begin{array}{r} 7 \\ + 8 \\ \hline \end{array} \quad
\begin{array}{r} 9 \\ + 2 \\ \hline \end{array} \quad
\begin{array}{r} 3 \\ + 7 \\ \hline \end{array} \quad
\begin{array}{r} 4 \\ + 6 \\ \hline \end{array} \quad
\begin{array}{r} 0 \\ + 8 \\ \hline \end{array} \quad
\begin{array}{r} 9 \\ + 8 \\ \hline \end{array}
$$

Addition Word Problems

Name_____ Date_____

Write and solve an addition equation for each problem.

1. The city zoo has four Asian elephants and five African elephants. How many elephants does it have in all?

   4 + 5 = 9

2. The parrot house has six adult macaws and nine young macaws. How many macaws does it have in all?

   ____ + ____ = ____

3. The Down Under Display has nine mother koalas. Three of them each have one baby. How many koalas are there in all?

   ____ + ____ = ____

4. Two large shallow pools hold seven white rhinos and six black rhinos. How many rhinos are there in all?

   ____ + ____ = ____

5. In the monkey house, there are eight tamarins and six marmosets. How many monkeys are there in all?

   ____ + ____ = ____

6. Last year, the anaconda snake measured nine feet long. This year it grew another nine feet. How many feet long is it this year?

   ____ + ____ = ____

7. The Polar Display has seven penguins and four harp seals. How many polar animals are there in all?

   ____ + ____ = ____

8. The seals eat eight baskets of fish a day. How many baskets of fish do they eat in two days?

   ____ + ____ = ____

Subtraction Terms

Name_____ Date_____

Look at the equation.

The **minuend** is the number being subtracted from.

The **subtrahend** is the number being subtracted.

The **difference** is the number that is left after subtracting.

$5 \longrightarrow$ **minuend**

$-1 \longrightarrow$ **subtrahend**

$4 \longrightarrow$ **difference**

Find the **difference**.

1.
$$\begin{array}{r} 5 \\ -4 \\ \hline \end{array} \qquad \begin{array}{r} 12 \\ -3 \\ \hline \end{array} \qquad \begin{array}{r} 10 \\ -5 \\ \hline \end{array} \qquad \begin{array}{r} 8 \\ -2 \\ \hline \end{array} \qquad \begin{array}{r} 1 \\ -0 \\ \hline \end{array} \qquad \begin{array}{r} 11 \\ -7 \\ \hline \end{array} \qquad \begin{array}{r} 7 \\ -4 \\ \hline \end{array}$$

2.
$$\begin{array}{r} 11 \\ -5 \\ \hline \end{array} \qquad \begin{array}{r} 2 \\ -1 \\ \hline \end{array} \qquad \begin{array}{r} 6 \\ -3 \\ \hline \end{array} \qquad \begin{array}{r} 9 \\ -4 \\ \hline \end{array} \qquad \begin{array}{r} 4 \\ -2 \\ \hline \end{array} \qquad \begin{array}{r} 12 \\ -8 \\ \hline \end{array} \qquad \begin{array}{r} 10 \\ -9 \\ \hline \end{array}$$

Find the missing **minuend**.

3.
$$\begin{array}{r} \square \\ -4 \\ \hline 4 \end{array} \qquad \begin{array}{r} \square \\ -5 \\ \hline 7 \end{array} \qquad \begin{array}{r} \square \\ -1 \\ \hline 9 \end{array} \qquad \begin{array}{r} \square \\ -7 \\ \hline 2 \end{array} \qquad \begin{array}{r} \square \\ -3 \\ \hline 8 \end{array} \qquad \begin{array}{r} \square \\ -0 \\ \hline 12 \end{array}$$

4.
$$\begin{array}{r} \square \\ -2 \\ \hline 9 \end{array} \qquad \begin{array}{r} \square \\ -8 \\ \hline 2 \end{array} \qquad \begin{array}{r} \square \\ -9 \\ \hline 3 \end{array} \qquad \begin{array}{r} \square \\ -6 \\ \hline 6 \end{array} \qquad \begin{array}{r} \square \\ -4 \\ \hline 3 \end{array} \qquad \begin{array}{r} \square \\ -2 \\ \hline 1 \end{array}$$

Find the missing **subtrahend**.

5.
$$\begin{array}{r} 12 \\ -\square \\ \hline 4 \end{array} \qquad \begin{array}{r} 8 \\ -\square \\ \hline 5 \end{array} \qquad \begin{array}{r} 5 \\ -\square \\ \hline 5 \end{array} \qquad \begin{array}{r} 11 \\ -\square \\ \hline 7 \end{array} \qquad \begin{array}{r} 6 \\ -\square \\ \hline 2 \end{array} \qquad \begin{array}{r} 4 \\ -\square \\ \hline 1 \end{array}$$

6.
$$\begin{array}{r} 7 \\ -\square \\ \hline 5 \end{array} \qquad \begin{array}{r} 10 \\ -\square \\ \hline 7 \end{array} \qquad \begin{array}{r} 3 \\ -\square \\ \hline 0 \end{array} \qquad \begin{array}{r} 9 \\ -\square \\ \hline 4 \end{array} \qquad \begin{array}{r} 2 \\ -\square \\ \hline 1 \end{array} \qquad \begin{array}{r} 12 \\ -\square \\ \hline 8 \end{array}$$

Subtraction Practice

Name_____ Date_____

Find the difference.

1. 7 – 4 = _____   12 – 5 = _____   2 – 2 = _____   9 – 3 = _____

2. 8 – 7 = _____   4 – 0 = _____   8 – 4 = _____   5 – 2 = _____

3. 7 – 1 = _____   10 – 2 = _____   16 – 7 = _____   3 – 3 = _____

4. 11 – 2 = _____   6 – 5 = _____   13 – 4 = _____   9 – 8 = _____

5.
$$\begin{array}{r} 1 \\ -\ 0 \\ \hline \end{array} \quad \begin{array}{r} 6 \\ -\ 6 \\ \hline \end{array} \quad \begin{array}{r} 17 \\ -\ 8 \\ \hline \end{array} \quad \begin{array}{r} 2 \\ -\ 1 \\ \hline \end{array} \quad \begin{array}{r} 10 \\ -\ 6 \\ \hline \end{array} \quad \begin{array}{r} 12 \\ -\ 8 \\ \hline \end{array} \quad \begin{array}{r} 14 \\ -\ 9 \\ \hline \end{array}$$

6.
$$\begin{array}{r} 17 \\ -\ 9 \\ \hline \end{array} \quad \begin{array}{r} 4 \\ -\ 4 \\ \hline \end{array} \quad \begin{array}{r} 2 \\ -\ 0 \\ \hline \end{array} \quad \begin{array}{r} 5 \\ -\ 3 \\ \hline \end{array} \quad \begin{array}{r} 8 \\ -\ 5 \\ \hline \end{array} \quad \begin{array}{r} 4 \\ -\ 3 \\ \hline \end{array} \quad \begin{array}{r} 10 \\ -\ 7 \\ \hline \end{array}$$

7.
$$\begin{array}{r} 12 \\ -\ 7 \\ \hline \end{array} \quad \begin{array}{r} 5 \\ -\ 1 \\ \hline \end{array} \quad \begin{array}{r} 9 \\ -\ 6 \\ \hline \end{array} \quad \begin{array}{r} 6 \\ -\ 4 \\ \hline \end{array} \quad \begin{array}{r} 14 \\ -\ 6 \\ \hline \end{array} \quad \begin{array}{r} 4 \\ -\ 2 \\ \hline \end{array} \quad \begin{array}{r} 6 \\ -\ 1 \\ \hline \end{array}$$

8.
$$\begin{array}{r} 4 \\ -\ 3 \\ \hline \end{array} \quad \begin{array}{r} 13 \\ -\ 6 \\ \hline \end{array} \quad \begin{array}{r} 16 \\ -\ 8 \\ \hline \end{array} \quad \begin{array}{r} 8 \\ -\ 4 \\ \hline \end{array} \quad \begin{array}{r} 16 \\ -\ 9 \\ \hline \end{array} \quad \begin{array}{r} 6 \\ -\ 2 \\ \hline \end{array} \quad \begin{array}{r} 12 \\ -\ 6 \\ \hline \end{array}$$

9.
$$\begin{array}{r} 3 \\ -\ 0 \\ \hline \end{array} \quad \begin{array}{r} 7 \\ -\ 5 \\ \hline \end{array} \quad \begin{array}{r} 11 \\ -\ 4 \\ \hline \end{array} \quad \begin{array}{r} 5 \\ -\ 5 \\ \hline \end{array} \quad \begin{array}{r} 13 \\ -\ 7 \\ \hline \end{array} \quad \begin{array}{r} 15 \\ -\ 8 \\ \hline \end{array} \quad \begin{array}{r} 14 \\ -\ 9 \\ \hline \end{array}$$

10.
$$\begin{array}{r} 6 \\ -\ 3 \\ \hline \end{array} \quad \begin{array}{r} 11 \\ -\ 5 \\ \hline \end{array} \quad \begin{array}{r} 9 \\ -\ 7 \\ \hline \end{array} \quad \begin{array}{r} 13 \\ -\ 5 \\ \hline \end{array} \quad \begin{array}{r} 3 \\ -\ 2 \\ \hline \end{array} \quad \begin{array}{r} 7 \\ -\ 3 \\ \hline \end{array} \quad \begin{array}{r} 18 \\ -\ 9 \\ \hline \end{array}$$

Subtraction Word Problems

Name_____ Date_____

Write and solve a subtraction equation for each problem.

1. Mrs. Rodriguez bought a nine-pack of chips. Her son Joe and his friends ate four packs. How many are left?

   $9 - 4 = 5$

2. To make dinner, Mrs. Rodriguez used eight of the twelve potatoes in a bag. How many are left?

   ___ – ___ = ___

3. Pork chops were on sale, so Mrs. Rodriguez bought seventeen. She froze nine for another day and cooked the rest. How many pork chops did she cook?

   ___ – ___ = ___

4. Mrs. Rodriguez had sixteen apples. She used nine to make a pie. How many apples are left?

   ___ – ___ = ___

5. The next morning, Mrs. Rodriguez scrambled seven of her dozen eggs. How many eggs are left?

   ___ – ___ = ___

6. Mrs. Rodriguez also toasted six of the thirteen slices of bread in a package. How many slices are left?

   ___ – ___ = ___

7. Mrs. Rodriguez cut a pineapple into fifteen pieces. Her family ate six. How many pieces are left?

   ___ – ___ = ___

8. A carton of juice held fourteen servings. The Rodriguez family drank five. How many servings are left?

   ___ – ___ = ___

Name_____ Date_____

Solve.

1.
$\begin{array}{r} 9 \\ + 0 \\ \hline \end{array}$
$\begin{array}{r} 4 \\ + 3 \\ \hline \end{array}$
$\begin{array}{r} 7 \\ + 0 \\ \hline \end{array}$
$\begin{array}{r} 5 \\ + 1 \\ \hline \end{array}$
$\begin{array}{r} 1 \\ + 6 \\ \hline \end{array}$
$\begin{array}{r} 8 \\ + 8 \\ \hline \end{array}$
$\begin{array}{r} 4 \\ + 9 \\ \hline \end{array}$
$\begin{array}{r} 5 \\ + 8 \\ \hline \end{array}$

2.
$\begin{array}{r} 3 \\ + 1 \\ \hline \end{array}$
$\begin{array}{r} 6 \\ + 4 \\ \hline \end{array}$
$\begin{array}{r} 2 \\ + 0 \\ \hline \end{array}$
$\begin{array}{r} 8 \\ + 7 \\ \hline \end{array}$
$\begin{array}{r} 4 \\ + 4 \\ \hline \end{array}$
$\begin{array}{r} 9 \\ + 8 \\ \hline \end{array}$
$\begin{array}{r} 5 \\ + 6 \\ \hline \end{array}$
$\begin{array}{r} 7 \\ + 9 \\ \hline \end{array}$

3.
$\begin{array}{r} 3 \\ + 6 \\ \hline \end{array}$
$\begin{array}{r} 8 \\ + 1 \\ \hline \end{array}$
$\begin{array}{r} 9 \\ + 2 \\ \hline \end{array}$
$\begin{array}{r} 3 \\ + 8 \\ \hline \end{array}$
$\begin{array}{r} 6 \\ + 5 \\ \hline \end{array}$
$\begin{array}{r} 4 \\ + 5 \\ \hline \end{array}$
$\begin{array}{r} 7 \\ + 7 \\ \hline \end{array}$
$\begin{array}{r} 9 \\ + 3 \\ \hline \end{array}$

4.
$\begin{array}{r} 7 \\ + 8 \\ \hline \end{array}$
$\begin{array}{r} 6 \\ + 9 \\ \hline \end{array}$
$\begin{array}{r} 5 \\ + 5 \\ \hline \end{array}$
$\begin{array}{r} 7 \\ + 1 \\ \hline \end{array}$
$\begin{array}{r} 2 \\ + 4 \\ \hline \end{array}$
$\begin{array}{r} 6 \\ + 7 \\ \hline \end{array}$
$\begin{array}{r} 2 \\ + 9 \\ \hline \end{array}$
$\begin{array}{r} 3 \\ + 5 \\ \hline \end{array}$

5.
$\begin{array}{r} 5 \\ + 7 \\ \hline \end{array}$
$\begin{array}{r} 1 \\ + 1 \\ \hline \end{array}$
$\begin{array}{r} 8 \\ + 6 \\ \hline \end{array}$
$\begin{array}{r} 8 \\ + 4 \\ \hline \end{array}$
$\begin{array}{r} 4 \\ + 6 \\ \hline \end{array}$
$\begin{array}{r} 8 \\ + 2 \\ \hline \end{array}$
$\begin{array}{r} 2 \\ + 1 \\ \hline \end{array}$
$\begin{array}{r} 9 \\ + 9 \\ \hline \end{array}$

6.
$\begin{array}{r} 12 \\ - 7 \\ \hline \end{array}$
$\begin{array}{r} 5 \\ - 1 \\ \hline \end{array}$
$\begin{array}{r} 9 \\ - 6 \\ \hline \end{array}$
$\begin{array}{r} 6 \\ - 4 \\ \hline \end{array}$
$\begin{array}{r} 14 \\ - 6 \\ \hline \end{array}$
$\begin{array}{r} 4 \\ - 2 \\ \hline \end{array}$
$\begin{array}{r} 10 \\ - 5 \\ \hline \end{array}$
$\begin{array}{r} 8 \\ - 1 \\ \hline \end{array}$

7.
$\begin{array}{r} 14 \\ - 8 \\ \hline \end{array}$
$\begin{array}{r} 7 \\ - 3 \\ \hline \end{array}$
$\begin{array}{r} 8 \\ - 4 \\ \hline \end{array}$
$\begin{array}{r} 15 \\ - 6 \\ \hline \end{array}$
$\begin{array}{r} 18 \\ - 9 \\ \hline \end{array}$
$\begin{array}{r} 11 \\ - 3 \\ \hline \end{array}$
$\begin{array}{r} 10 \\ - 2 \\ \hline \end{array}$
$\begin{array}{r} 9 \\ - 5 \\ \hline \end{array}$

8.
$\begin{array}{r} 16 \\ - 9 \\ \hline \end{array}$
$\begin{array}{r} 12 \\ - 5 \\ \hline \end{array}$
$\begin{array}{r} 7 \\ - 6 \\ \hline \end{array}$
$\begin{array}{r} 13 \\ - 4 \\ \hline \end{array}$
$\begin{array}{r} 6 \\ - 6 \\ \hline \end{array}$
$\begin{array}{r} 15 \\ - 8 \\ \hline \end{array}$
$\begin{array}{r} 11 \\ - 5 \\ \hline \end{array}$
$\begin{array}{r} 14 \\ - 7 \\ \hline \end{array}$

9.
$\begin{array}{r} 16 \\ - 8 \\ \hline \end{array}$
$\begin{array}{r} 17 \\ - 9 \\ \hline \end{array}$
$\begin{array}{r} 12 \\ - 6 \\ \hline \end{array}$
$\begin{array}{r} 8 \\ - 5 \\ \hline \end{array}$
$\begin{array}{r} 15 \\ - 9 \\ \hline \end{array}$
$\begin{array}{r} 16 \\ - 7 \\ \hline \end{array}$
$\begin{array}{r} 5 \\ - 3 \\ \hline \end{array}$
$\begin{array}{r} 13 \\ - 5 \\ \hline \end{array}$

10.
$\begin{array}{r} 14 \\ - 9 \\ \hline \end{array}$
$\begin{array}{r} 15 \\ - 7 \\ \hline \end{array}$
$\begin{array}{r} 11 \\ - 6 \\ \hline \end{array}$
$\begin{array}{r} 17 \\ - 8 \\ \hline \end{array}$
$\begin{array}{r} 7 \\ - 2 \\ \hline \end{array}$
$\begin{array}{r} 14 \\ - 5 \\ \hline \end{array}$
$\begin{array}{r} 12 \\ - 3 \\ \hline \end{array}$
$\begin{array}{r} 10 \\ - 3 \\ \hline \end{array}$

Name_____ Date_____

Read each problem and write an equation to solve it.
Circle **A** if the problem required addition or **S** if it required subtraction.

1. The Tigers scored nine runs in the first game of the season and seven in the second. How many runs did they score in both games?

   A   **S**

   ____ $+/-$ ____ = ____

2. The Falcons lost the first six of their fourteen games but won the rest. How many games did they win?

   A   **S**

   ____ $+/-$ ____ = ____

3. Two of the players on the Bulldogs team needed new caps. The caps cost eight dollars apiece. How much did the two caps cost in all?

   A   **S**

   ____ $+/-$ ____ = ____

4. In one inning, the Lions had nine hits and the Eagles had four. How many total hits were made in the inning?

   A   **S**

   ____ $+/-$ ____ = ____

5. Mr. Jones coached the Panthers for eight of their seventeen games. Mrs. Lee coached the rest. How many games did she coach?

   A   **S**

   ____ $+/-$ ____ = ____

6. When the Tigers played the Panthers, the Tigers had six walks. The Panthers had seven. How many walks were there in all?

   A   **S**

   ____ $+/-$ ____ = ____

Checking Subtraction

Name_____ Date_____

Solve each subtraction problem. Then check your answer by adding the subtrahend to the difference.

1.
```
   15        9
 -  6   +   6
 [ 9 ]     [15]
```
```
   10       □
 -  3   +   □
   □        □
```
```
    9       □
 -  2   +   □
   □        □
```

2.
```
   11       □
 -  5   +   □
   □        □
```
```
    9       □
 -  0   +   □
   □        □
```
```
    7       □
 -  4   +   □
   □        □
```

3.
```
    8       □
 -  7   +   □
   □        □
```
```
   18       □
 -  9   +   □
   □        □
```
```
   14       □
 -  5   +   □
   □        □
```

4.
```
   16       □
 -  9   +   □
   □        □
```
```
   13       □
 -  6   +   □
   □        □
```
```
   11       □
 -  8   +   □
   □        □
```

5.
```
    4       □
 -  1   +   □
   □        □
```
```
   17       □
 -  8   +   □
   □        □
```
```
   12       □
 -  4   +   □
   □        □
```

6.
```
   10       □
 -  5   +   □
   □        □
```
```
   15       □
 -  7   +   □
   □        □
```
```
    8       □
 -  3   +   □
   □        □
```

Name_____ Date_____

$$
\begin{array}{r}
45 \\
+\ 3 \\
\hline
48
\end{array}
$$
First, add the ones.

Then add the tens.
$$
\begin{array}{r}
45 \\
+\ 3 \\
\hline
48
\end{array}
$$

Find the sum.

1.
$$
\begin{array}{r} 23 \\ +\ 6 \\ \hline \end{array}
\qquad
\begin{array}{r} 81 \\ +\ 7 \\ \hline \end{array}
\qquad
\begin{array}{r} 64 \\ +\ 4 \\ \hline \end{array}
\qquad
\begin{array}{r} 12 \\ +\ 5 \\ \hline \end{array}
\qquad
\begin{array}{r} 52 \\ +\ 3 \\ \hline \end{array}
\qquad
\begin{array}{r} 67 \\ +\ 0 \\ \hline \end{array}
$$

2.
$$
\begin{array}{r} 90 \\ +\ 9 \\ \hline \end{array}
\qquad
\begin{array}{r} 76 \\ +\ 2 \\ \hline \end{array}
\qquad
\begin{array}{r} 22 \\ +\ 7 \\ \hline \end{array}
\qquad
\begin{array}{r} 30 \\ +\ 8 \\ \hline \end{array}
\qquad
\begin{array}{r} 15 \\ +\ 4 \\ \hline \end{array}
\qquad
\begin{array}{r} 28 \\ +\ 1 \\ \hline \end{array}
$$

3.
$$
\begin{array}{r} 35 \\ +\ 4 \\ \hline \end{array}
\qquad
\begin{array}{r} 42 \\ +\ 5 \\ \hline \end{array}
\qquad
\begin{array}{r} 17 \\ +\ 2 \\ \hline \end{array}
\qquad
\begin{array}{r} 61 \\ +\ 8 \\ \hline \end{array}
\qquad
\begin{array}{r} 11 \\ +\ 5 \\ \hline \end{array}
\qquad
\begin{array}{r} 87 \\ +\ 1 \\ \hline \end{array}
$$

4.
$$
\begin{array}{r} 10 \\ +\ 9 \\ \hline \end{array}
\qquad
\begin{array}{r} 56 \\ +\ 3 \\ \hline \end{array}
\qquad
\begin{array}{r} 14 \\ +\ 5 \\ \hline \end{array}
\qquad
\begin{array}{r} 63 \\ +\ 3 \\ \hline \end{array}
\qquad
\begin{array}{r} 19 \\ +\ 0 \\ \hline \end{array}
\qquad
\begin{array}{r} 82 \\ +\ 4 \\ \hline \end{array}
$$

Read each problem and write an equation to solve it.

5. Kim's math test grade was 84, but she received five extra points for answering a bonus question correctly. What was her final grade?

____ + ____ = ____

6. John's grade was 91, and he also answered the bonus question correctly. What was John's final grade?

____ + ____ = ____

7. Twenty students passed the math test. Three did not. How many students took the test?

____ + ____ = ____

Adding Ones and Tens (II)

Name_____ Date_____

Find the sum.

1.
$$31 + 8$$ $$78 + 1$$ $$24 + 1$$ $$15 + 3$$ $$50 + 8$$ $$13 + 6$$

2.
$$64 + 2$$ $$33 + 5$$ $$27 + 1$$ $$18 + 0$$ $$41 + 7$$ $$20 + 8$$

3.
$$92 + 4$$ $$65 + 2$$ $$16 + 2$$ $$23 + 6$$ $$84 + 4$$ $$12 + 3$$

4.
$$56 + 1$$ $$74 + 3$$ $$91 + 8$$ $$82 + 5$$ $$14 + 5$$ $$36 + 3$$

Find the missing addend.

5. $34 + \boxed{} = 38$ $46 + \boxed{} = 49$ $19 + \boxed{} = 19$

6. $\boxed{} + 94 = 97$ $\boxed{} + 62 = 69$ $\boxed{} + 11 = 18$

Read the problem and write an equation to solve it.

7. Emir had twenty-two CDs. He just bought seven more.
How many CDs does he now have in all?   ____ + ____ = ____

Name_____ Date_____

```
  48
-  3
─────
  45     First, subtract the ones.     Then subtract the tens.
```
```
  48
-  3
─────
  45
```

Find the difference.

1.
```
  29        76        88        17        45        33
-  5      -  3      -  7      -  4      -  2      -  1
────      ────      ────      ────      ────      ────
```

2.
```
  12        38        19        24        67        99
-  1      -  6      -  9      -  3      -  5      -  8
────      ────      ────      ────      ────      ────
```

3.
```
  47        59        13        26        35        56
-  7      -  2      -  2      -  5      -  4      -  3
────      ────      ────      ────      ────      ────
```

4.
```
  15        47        39        66        78        85
-  2      -  6      -  7      -  1      -  8      -  3
────      ────      ────      ────      ────      ────
```

Read each problem and write an equation to solve it.

5. Hank had 68 trading cards. He gave six to his
   friend, Jesse. How many cards does Hank have left?   _____ − _____ = _____

6. Jesse had 49 trading cards, but he lost eight of
   them through a hole in his backpack. How many
   cards does he have left?

7. Tyrone's puppy chewed seven of his 59 trading cards.
   How many cards does Tyrone have left?

Name_____ Date_____

Find the difference.

1.
```
  55      47      68      21      96      87
 - 5     - 6     - 3     - 1     - 4     - 7
```

2.
```
  64      86      97      26      33      18
 - 3     - 5     - 4     - 2     - 2     - 7
```

3.
```
  75      43      19      28      94      29
 - 3     - 0     - 7     - 5     - 2     - 4
```

4.
```
  57      68      72      16      26      85
 - 2     - 6     - 2     - 3     - 5     - 3
```

Find the missing minuend or subtrahend.

5. $\boxed{} - 5 = 63$ $\boxed{} - 7 = 22$ $\boxed{} - 4 = 13$

6. $46 - \boxed{} = 40$ $84 - \boxed{} = 81$ $78 - \boxed{} = 73$

Read the problem and write an equation to solve it.

7. Sarah read seven pages of her 48-page book.   ____ – ____ = ____
   How many pages does she have left to read?

Name_____ Date_____

Solve.

1.
$$\begin{array}{r} 7 \\ + 5 \\ \hline \end{array}$$
$$\begin{array}{r} 6 \\ + 8 \\ \hline \end{array}$$
$$\begin{array}{r} 9 \\ + 4 \\ \hline \end{array}$$
$$\begin{array}{r} 5 \\ + 6 \\ \hline \end{array}$$
$$\begin{array}{r} 6 \\ + 7 \\ \hline \end{array}$$
$$\begin{array}{r} 8 \\ + 3 \\ \hline \end{array}$$

2.
$$\begin{array}{r} 3 \\ + 9 \\ \hline \end{array}$$
$$\begin{array}{r} 8 \\ + 8 \\ \hline \end{array}$$
$$\begin{array}{r} 4 \\ + 7 \\ \hline \end{array}$$
$$\begin{array}{r} 9 \\ + 7 \\ \hline \end{array}$$
$$\begin{array}{r} 7 \\ + 7 \\ \hline \end{array}$$
$$\begin{array}{r} 6 \\ + 5 \\ \hline \end{array}$$

3.
$$\begin{array}{r} 84 \\ + 4 \\ \hline \end{array}$$
$$\begin{array}{r} 56 \\ + 3 \\ \hline \end{array}$$
$$\begin{array}{r} 13 \\ + 1 \\ \hline \end{array}$$
$$\begin{array}{r} 40 \\ + 9 \\ \hline \end{array}$$
$$\begin{array}{r} 32 \\ + 7 \\ \hline \end{array}$$
$$\begin{array}{r} 63 \\ + 4 \\ \hline \end{array}$$

4.
$$\begin{array}{r} 28 \\ + 1 \\ \hline \end{array}$$
$$\begin{array}{r} 93 \\ + 3 \\ \hline \end{array}$$
$$\begin{array}{r} 82 \\ + 3 \\ \hline \end{array}$$
$$\begin{array}{r} 60 \\ + 5 \\ \hline \end{array}$$
$$\begin{array}{r} 25 \\ + 4 \\ \hline \end{array}$$
$$\begin{array}{r} 14 \\ + 3 \\ \hline \end{array}$$

5.
$$\begin{array}{r} 12 \\ + 7 \\ \hline \end{array}$$
$$\begin{array}{r} 54 \\ + 0 \\ \hline \end{array}$$
$$\begin{array}{r} 76 \\ + 1 \\ \hline \end{array}$$
$$\begin{array}{r} 20 \\ + 8 \\ \hline \end{array}$$
$$\begin{array}{r} 11 \\ + 8 \\ \hline \end{array}$$
$$\begin{array}{r} 94 \\ + 5 \\ \hline \end{array}$$

6.
$$\begin{array}{r} 16 \\ - 7 \\ \hline \end{array}$$
$$\begin{array}{r} 18 \\ - 9 \\ \hline \end{array}$$
$$\begin{array}{r} 17 \\ - 8 \\ \hline \end{array}$$
$$\begin{array}{r} 12 \\ - 7 \\ \hline \end{array}$$
$$\begin{array}{r} 13 \\ - 6 \\ \hline \end{array}$$
$$\begin{array}{r} 15 \\ - 8 \\ \hline \end{array}$$

7.
$$\begin{array}{r} 14 \\ - 5 \\ \hline \end{array}$$
$$\begin{array}{r} 11 \\ - 4 \\ \hline \end{array}$$
$$\begin{array}{r} 15 \\ - 6 \\ \hline \end{array}$$
$$\begin{array}{r} 16 \\ - 8 \\ \hline \end{array}$$
$$\begin{array}{r} 10 \\ - 4 \\ \hline \end{array}$$
$$\begin{array}{r} 12 \\ - 3 \\ \hline \end{array}$$

8.
$$\begin{array}{r} 58 \\ - 4 \\ \hline \end{array}$$
$$\begin{array}{r} 79 \\ - 9 \\ \hline \end{array}$$
$$\begin{array}{r} 36 \\ - 2 \\ \hline \end{array}$$
$$\begin{array}{r} 22 \\ - 1 \\ \hline \end{array}$$
$$\begin{array}{r} 17 \\ - 7 \\ \hline \end{array}$$
$$\begin{array}{r} 47 \\ - 5 \\ \hline \end{array}$$

9.
$$\begin{array}{r} 85 \\ - 3 \\ \hline \end{array}$$
$$\begin{array}{r} 38 \\ - 7 \\ \hline \end{array}$$
$$\begin{array}{r} 96 \\ - 5 \\ \hline \end{array}$$
$$\begin{array}{r} 16 \\ - 4 \\ \hline \end{array}$$
$$\begin{array}{r} 44 \\ - 3 \\ \hline \end{array}$$
$$\begin{array}{r} 89 \\ - 7 \\ \hline \end{array}$$

10.
$$\begin{array}{r} 15 \\ - 4 \\ \hline \end{array}$$
$$\begin{array}{r} 75 \\ - 5 \\ \hline \end{array}$$
$$\begin{array}{r} 48 \\ - 6 \\ \hline \end{array}$$
$$\begin{array}{r} 29 \\ - 2 \\ \hline \end{array}$$
$$\begin{array}{r} 55 \\ - 5 \\ \hline \end{array}$$
$$\begin{array}{r} 98 \\ - 7 \\ \hline \end{array}$$

Name_____ Date_____

Read each problem. Fill in the circle next to the equation that shows both the best way to solve the problem and the correct answer.

1. On Monday, the candy store owner sold six of the thirty-nine boxes of peanut chews on the shelf. How many boxes were left?
   ○ a) $6 + 33 = 39$ ○ b) $39 - 6 = 33$ ○ c) $39 - 33 = 6$ ○ d) $39 + 6 = 45$

2. Mrs. Dixon bought fifteen chocolate bars with almonds and four without almonds. How many chocolate bars did she buy in all?
   ○ a) $19 - 4 = 15$ ○ b) $15 + 4 = 20$ ○ c) $15 + 4 = 19$ ○ d) $19 - 15 = 4$

3. Jimmy bought a candy bar for fifty-two cents and a gumball for five cents. How many cents did his treats cost in all?
   ○ a) $52 - 5 = 47$ ○ b) $52 + 5 = 59$ ○ c) $57 - 5 = 52$ ○ d) $52 + 5 = 57$

4. Alison bought a twelve-pack of gum, and gave four pieces to her little brother. How many pieces did she have left?
   ○ a) $12 - 4 = 8$ ○ b) $12 - 8 = 4$ ○ c) $12 + 4 = 16$ ○ d) $4 + 8 = 12$

5. The storeowner sold seven pounds of white chocolate and nine pounds of dark chocolate. How many pounds of chocolate were sold?
   ○ a) $9 - 7 = 2$ ○ b) $7 + 9 = 16$ ○ c) $7 + 9 = 17$ ○ d) $7 + 9 = 15$

6. Mr. Parson bought fifteen candy gift boxes, but later returned six to the store. How many boxes did he keep?
   ○ a) $15 + 6 = 21$ ○ b) $21 - 6 = 15$ ○ c) $15 - 6 = 8$ ○ d) $15 - 6 = 9$

7. Each box of saltwater taffy holds thirty-eight pieces. In each box, there are seven white pieces. How many pieces are not white?
   ○ a) $38 + 7 = 45$ ○ b) $38 - 7 = 32$ ○ c) $38 - 7 = 31$ ○ d) $38 - 31 = 7$

8. There are twelve jars of solid-colored jelly beans and six jars of speckled jelly beans. How many jars of jelly beans in all?
   ○ a) $12 - 6 = 6$ ○ b) $12 + 6 = 17$ ○ c) $12 + 6 = 20$ ○ d) $12 + 6 = 18$

Addition: Regrouping (I)

Name_____ Date_____

$$\begin{array}{r} \overset{1}{3}6 \\ +\ 9 \\ \hline 7 \end{array}$$

First add the ones.
Regroup 17 as 1 ten and 7 ones.
Then add the tens.

$$\begin{array}{r} \overset{1}{3}6 \\ +\ 9 \\ \hline 47 \end{array}$$

Write the amount of tens and ones in each number.

1. 42 = _4_ tens + _2_ ones   63 = ___ tens + ___ ones   37 = ___ tens + ___ ones

2. 55 = ___ tens + ___ ones   28 = ___ tens + ___ ones   74 = ___ tens + ___ ones

3. 21 = ___ tens + ___ ones   86 = ___ tens + ___ ones   19 = ___ tens + ___ ones

Add.

4.
$$\begin{array}{r} 42 \\ +\ 9 \\ \hline \end{array} \qquad \begin{array}{r} 63 \\ +\ 7 \\ \hline \end{array} \qquad \begin{array}{r} 37 \\ +\ 5 \\ \hline \end{array} \qquad \begin{array}{r} 55 \\ +\ 6 \\ \hline \end{array} \qquad \begin{array}{r} 28 \\ +\ 3 \\ \hline \end{array} \qquad \begin{array}{r} 74 \\ +\ 8 \\ \hline \end{array}$$

5.
$$\begin{array}{r} 21 \\ +\ 9 \\ \hline \end{array} \qquad \begin{array}{r} 86 \\ +\ 9 \\ \hline \end{array} \qquad \begin{array}{r} 19 \\ +\ 3 \\ \hline \end{array} \qquad \begin{array}{r} 78 \\ +\ 8 \\ \hline \end{array} \qquad \begin{array}{r} 57 \\ +\ 6 \\ \hline \end{array} \qquad \begin{array}{r} 28 \\ +\ 7 \\ \hline \end{array}$$

6.
$$\begin{array}{r} 18 \\ +\ 6 \\ \hline \end{array} \qquad \begin{array}{r} 74 \\ +\ 9 \\ \hline \end{array} \qquad \begin{array}{r} 26 \\ +\ 8 \\ \hline \end{array} \qquad \begin{array}{r} 85 \\ +\ 5 \\ \hline \end{array} \qquad \begin{array}{r} 25 \\ +\ 9 \\ \hline \end{array} \qquad \begin{array}{r} 76 \\ +\ 7 \\ \hline \end{array}$$

7.
$$\begin{array}{r} 47 \\ +\ 3 \\ \hline \end{array} \qquad \begin{array}{r} 24 \\ +\ 8 \\ \hline \end{array} \qquad \begin{array}{r} 86 \\ +\ 6 \\ \hline \end{array} \qquad \begin{array}{r} 38 \\ +\ 7 \\ \hline \end{array} \qquad \begin{array}{r} 11 \\ +\ 9 \\ \hline \end{array} \qquad \begin{array}{r} 46 \\ +\ 9 \\ \hline \end{array}$$

Addition Practice (I)

Name_____ Date_____

Add.

1.
$$38 + 8$$ $$25 + 5$$ $$61 + 9$$ $$87 + 4$$ $$16 + 6$$ $$82 + 8$$

2.
$$17 + 8$$ $$67 + 5$$ $$53 + 9$$ $$73 + 7$$ $$49 + 2$$ $$18 + 8$$

3.
$$37 + 4$$ $$49 + 1$$ $$52 + 9$$ $$79 + 3$$ $$14 + 6$$ $$38 + 5$$

4.
$$77 + 3$$ $$86 + 5$$ $$32 + 9$$ $$54 + 8$$ $$79 + 5$$ $$15 + 7$$

5.
$$12 + 5 + 3$$ $$57 + 3 + 4$$ $$39 + 1 + 6$$ $$61 + 4 + 6$$ $$86 + 9 + 2$$ $$43 + 7 + 4$$

6.
$$83 + 9 + 2$$ $$35 + 5 + 5$$ $$10 + 6 + 8$$ $$79 + 3 + 1$$ $$12 + 7 + 6$$ $$28 + 2 + 7$$

7.
$$14 + 4 + 4$$ $$86 + 3 + 9$$ $$44 + 5 + 2$$ $$19 + 8 + 1$$ $$58 + 3 + 4$$ $$55 + 9 + 3$$

Name_____ Date_____

Write and solve an addition equation for each problem.

1. Last year, Denise weighed 62 pounds. This year she weighs nine pounds more. How many pounds does she weigh this year?

2. David weighed 74 pounds last year. This year he gained eight pounds. How many pounds does he weigh this year?

3. Brittany weighed 58 pounds last year. She gained three pounds by spring and another five pounds over the summer. How many pounds does she weigh now?

4. Andy was 46 inches tall last year. This year he has grown seven inches. How many inches tall is Andy this year?

5. Janelle grew six inches this year. Last year she was 45 inches tall. How many inches tall is she this year?

6. Fred was 50 inches tall last year. He grew seven inches in eight months and another three inches in the last four months. How many inches tall is Fred now?

Subtraction: Regrouping (I)

Name_____ Date_____

$$\begin{array}{r} {}^{2}\cancel{3}{}^{16} \\ -9 \\ \hline 7 \end{array}$$

First regroup the tens and ones, borrowing one ten for the ones place. Subtract the ones. Then subtract the tens.

$$\begin{array}{r} {}^{2}\cancel{3}{}^{16} \\ -9 \\ \hline 27 \end{array}$$

Subtract.

1.
$$\begin{array}{r} 37 \\ -9 \\ \hline \end{array}$$
$$\begin{array}{r} 21 \\ -3 \\ \hline \end{array}$$
$$\begin{array}{r} 64 \\ -5 \\ \hline \end{array}$$
$$\begin{array}{r} 72 \\ -4 \\ \hline \end{array}$$
$$\begin{array}{r} 50 \\ -3 \\ \hline \end{array}$$
$$\begin{array}{r} 91 \\ -5 \\ \hline \end{array}$$

2.
$$\begin{array}{r} 46 \\ -8 \\ \hline \end{array}$$
$$\begin{array}{r} 19 \\ -6 \\ \hline \end{array}$$
$$\begin{array}{r} 26 \\ -9 \\ \hline \end{array}$$
$$\begin{array}{r} 83 \\ -4 \\ \hline \end{array}$$
$$\begin{array}{r} 35 \\ -7 \\ \hline \end{array}$$
$$\begin{array}{r} 28 \\ -9 \\ \hline \end{array}$$

3.
$$\begin{array}{r} 94 \\ -8 \\ \hline \end{array}$$
$$\begin{array}{r} 20 \\ -1 \\ \hline \end{array}$$
$$\begin{array}{r} 87 \\ -9 \\ \hline \end{array}$$
$$\begin{array}{r} 33 \\ -6 \\ \hline \end{array}$$
$$\begin{array}{r} 78 \\ -9 \\ \hline \end{array}$$
$$\begin{array}{r} 41 \\ -2 \\ \hline \end{array}$$

4.
$$\begin{array}{r} 60 \\ -5 \\ \hline \end{array}$$
$$\begin{array}{r} 52 \\ -4 \\ \hline \end{array}$$
$$\begin{array}{r} 97 \\ -8 \\ \hline \end{array}$$
$$\begin{array}{r} 23 \\ -5 \\ \hline \end{array}$$
$$\begin{array}{r} 82 \\ -9 \\ \hline \end{array}$$
$$\begin{array}{r} 36 \\ -8 \\ \hline \end{array}$$

5.
$$\begin{array}{r} 75 \\ -6 \\ \hline \end{array}$$
$$\begin{array}{r} 42 \\ -5 \\ \hline \end{array}$$
$$\begin{array}{r} 65 \\ -7 \\ \hline \end{array}$$
$$\begin{array}{r} 80 \\ -2 \\ \hline \end{array}$$
$$\begin{array}{r} 57 \\ -8 \\ \hline \end{array}$$
$$\begin{array}{r} 22 \\ -7 \\ \hline \end{array}$$

6.
$$\begin{array}{r} 96 \\ -8 \\ \hline \end{array}$$
$$\begin{array}{r} 24 \\ -5 \\ \hline \end{array}$$
$$\begin{array}{r} 85 \\ -8 \\ \hline \end{array}$$
$$\begin{array}{r} 38 \\ -9 \\ \hline \end{array}$$
$$\begin{array}{r} 74 \\ -6 \\ \hline \end{array}$$
$$\begin{array}{r} 45 \\ -6 \\ \hline \end{array}$$

7.
$$\begin{array}{r} 66 \\ -7 \\ \hline \end{array}$$
$$\begin{array}{r} 55 \\ -7 \\ \hline \end{array}$$
$$\begin{array}{r} 20 \\ -4 \\ \hline \end{array}$$
$$\begin{array}{r} 92 \\ -8 \\ \hline \end{array}$$
$$\begin{array}{r} 34 \\ -7 \\ \hline \end{array}$$
$$\begin{array}{r} 81 \\ -9 \\ \hline \end{array}$$

8.
$$\begin{array}{r} 22 \\ -9 \\ \hline \end{array}$$
$$\begin{array}{r} 31 \\ -7 \\ \hline \end{array}$$
$$\begin{array}{r} 76 \\ -8 \\ \hline \end{array}$$
$$\begin{array}{r} 47 \\ -9 \\ \hline \end{array}$$
$$\begin{array}{r} 63 \\ -8 \\ \hline \end{array}$$
$$\begin{array}{r} 57 \\ -9 \\ \hline \end{array}$$

Subtraction Practice (I)

Name_____ Date_____

Subtract.

1.
$$50 - 9$$ $$98 - 9$$ $$24 - 7$$ $$83 - 4$$ $$36 - 3$$ $$75 - 6$$

2.
$$62 - 3$$ $$51 - 5$$ $$20 - 9$$ $$74 - 5$$ $$32 - 7$$ $$85 - 8$$

3.
$$46 - 8$$ $$77 - 9$$ $$53 - 9$$ $$61 - 6$$ $$25 - 7$$ $$96 - 7$$

4.
$$31 - 4$$ $$70 - 4$$ $$27 - 8$$ $$55 - 9$$ $$43 - 8$$ $$72 - 8$$

Check each equation. If the answer is correct, circle **C**. If it is not correct, circle **NC** and then write the correct answer on the line.

5.
$$\begin{array}{r} 54 \\ -\ 8 \\ \hline 42 \end{array}$$ $$\begin{array}{r} 32 \\ -\ 7 \\ \hline 25 \end{array}$$ $$\begin{array}{r} 81 \\ -\ 7 \\ \hline 74 \end{array}$$ $$\begin{array}{r} 94 \\ -\ 5 \\ \hline 88 \end{array}$$

C (NC) 46   C NC____   C NC____   C NC____

6.
$$\begin{array}{r} 23 \\ -\ 6 \\ \hline 17 \end{array}$$ $$\begin{array}{r} 67 \\ -\ 9 \\ \hline 56 \end{array}$$ $$\begin{array}{r} 45 \\ -\ 7 \\ \hline 33 \end{array}$$ $$\begin{array}{r} 76 \\ -\ 8 \\ \hline 66 \end{array}$$

C NC____   C NC____   C NC____   C NC____

Subtraction Word Problems

Name_____ Date_____

Write and solve a subtraction equation for each problem.

1. Of the fifty-six problems on the math quiz, Jamal answered all but seven correctly. How many did he get right?

2. Leslie answered nine problems incorrectly. How many problems did she get right?

3. Out of twenty-two students, nine received a C on the quiz. How many students did not receive a C?

4. The next math quiz had sixty-one problems. Jamal answered only two problems incorrectly. How many did he get right?

5. On this same quiz, Leslie answered only four problems incorrectly. How many of her answers were correct?

6. Of the twenty-two students, only three received a C on this quiz. How many did not receive a C?

7. Nine students received a B. How many did not receive a B?

Addition

Name_____ Date_____

$$\begin{array}{r} 3\mathbf{6} \\ +1\mathbf{2} \\ \hline \mathbf{8} \end{array}$$ First, add the ones.   Then add the tens. $$\begin{array}{r} \mathbf{3}6 \\ +\mathbf{1}2 \\ \hline \mathbf{4}8 \end{array}$$

Add.

1. $\begin{array}{r} 30 \\ +30 \\ \hline \end{array}$ $\begin{array}{r} 50 \\ +10 \\ \hline \end{array}$ $\begin{array}{r} 70 \\ +20 \\ \hline \end{array}$ $\begin{array}{r} 10 \\ +40 \\ \hline \end{array}$ $\begin{array}{r} 80 \\ +12 \\ \hline \end{array}$ $\begin{array}{r} 60 \\ +38 \\ \hline \end{array}$

2. $\begin{array}{r} 40 \\ +15 \\ \hline \end{array}$ $\begin{array}{r} 20 \\ +72 \\ \hline \end{array}$ $\begin{array}{r} 30 \\ +49 \\ \hline \end{array}$ $\begin{array}{r} 73 \\ +25 \\ \hline \end{array}$ $\begin{array}{r} 44 \\ +55 \\ \hline \end{array}$ $\begin{array}{r} 31 \\ +27 \\ \hline \end{array}$

3. $\begin{array}{r} 83 \\ +14 \\ \hline \end{array}$ $\begin{array}{r} 37 \\ +51 \\ \hline \end{array}$ $\begin{array}{r} 11 \\ +77 \\ \hline \end{array}$ $\begin{array}{r} 45 \\ +13 \\ \hline \end{array}$ $\begin{array}{r} 52 \\ +24 \\ \hline \end{array}$ $\begin{array}{r} 36 \\ +31 \\ \hline \end{array}$

4. $\begin{array}{r} 63 \\ +24 \\ \hline \end{array}$ $\begin{array}{r} 24 \\ +62 \\ \hline \end{array}$ $\begin{array}{r} 58 \\ +21 \\ \hline \end{array}$ $\begin{array}{r} 29 \\ +10 \\ \hline \end{array}$ $\begin{array}{r} 22 \\ +73 \\ \hline \end{array}$ $\begin{array}{r} 81 \\ +16 \\ \hline \end{array}$

5. $\begin{array}{r} 42 \\ +15 \\ \hline \end{array}$ $\begin{array}{r} 55 \\ +32 \\ \hline \end{array}$ $\begin{array}{r} 38 \\ +61 \\ \hline \end{array}$ $\begin{array}{r} 27 \\ +32 \\ \hline \end{array}$ $\begin{array}{r} 82 \\ +13 \\ \hline \end{array}$ $\begin{array}{r} 44 \\ +23 \\ \hline \end{array}$

6. $\begin{array}{r} 16 \\ +32 \\ \hline \end{array}$ $\begin{array}{r} 30 \\ +17 \\ \hline \end{array}$ $\begin{array}{r} 10 \\ +74 \\ \hline \end{array}$ $\begin{array}{r} 14 \\ +54 \\ \hline \end{array}$ $\begin{array}{r} 87 \\ +11 \\ \hline \end{array}$ $\begin{array}{r} 13 \\ +46 \\ \hline \end{array}$

7. $\begin{array}{r} 17 \\ +12 \\ \hline \end{array}$ $\begin{array}{r} 65 \\ +33 \\ \hline \end{array}$ $\begin{array}{r} 72 \\ +27 \\ \hline \end{array}$ $\begin{array}{r} 51 \\ +38 \\ \hline \end{array}$ $\begin{array}{r} 34 \\ +43 \\ \hline \end{array}$ $\begin{array}{r} 63 \\ +13 \\ \hline \end{array}$

Addition: Regrouping (II)

Name_____ Date_____

$$\begin{array}{r}\overset{1}{3}6\\+15\\\hline 1\end{array}$$

First add the ones.

Regroup 11 as 1 ten and 1 ones.

Then add the tens.

$$\begin{array}{r}\overset{1}{\mathbf{3}}6\\+15\\\hline \mathbf{5}1\end{array}$$

Add.

1.
$\begin{array}{r}13\\+18\end{array}$
$\begin{array}{r}24\\+26\end{array}$
$\begin{array}{r}18\\+33\end{array}$
$\begin{array}{r}45\\+45\end{array}$
$\begin{array}{r}39\\+24\end{array}$
$\begin{array}{r}62\\+29\end{array}$

2.
$\begin{array}{r}75\\+17\end{array}$
$\begin{array}{r}46\\+38\end{array}$
$\begin{array}{r}64\\+27\end{array}$
$\begin{array}{r}38\\+25\end{array}$
$\begin{array}{r}29\\+58\end{array}$
$\begin{array}{r}67\\+28\end{array}$

3.
$\begin{array}{r}55\\+26\end{array}$
$\begin{array}{r}39\\+51\end{array}$
$\begin{array}{r}14\\+79\end{array}$
$\begin{array}{r}46\\+29\end{array}$
$\begin{array}{r}31\\+49\end{array}$
$\begin{array}{r}24\\+57\end{array}$

4.
$\begin{array}{r}62\\+18\end{array}$
$\begin{array}{r}25\\+52\end{array}$
$\begin{array}{r}57\\+26\end{array}$
$\begin{array}{r}35\\+15\end{array}$
$\begin{array}{r}47\\+35\end{array}$
$\begin{array}{r}28\\+48\end{array}$

5.
$\begin{array}{r}35\\+58\end{array}$
$\begin{array}{r}19\\+39\end{array}$
$\begin{array}{r}57\\+37\end{array}$
$\begin{array}{r}36\\+36\end{array}$
$\begin{array}{r}18\\+47\end{array}$
$\begin{array}{r}17\\+19\end{array}$

6.
$\begin{array}{r}22\\+49\end{array}$
$\begin{array}{r}33\\+58\end{array}$
$\begin{array}{r}48\\+23\end{array}$
$\begin{array}{r}16\\+54\end{array}$
$\begin{array}{r}15\\+15\end{array}$
$\begin{array}{r}28\\+42\end{array}$

7.
$\begin{array}{r}13\\+79\end{array}$
$\begin{array}{r}56\\+26\end{array}$
$\begin{array}{r}58\\+29\end{array}$
$\begin{array}{r}74\\+18\end{array}$
$\begin{array}{r}39\\+46\end{array}$
$\begin{array}{r}35\\+48\end{array}$

Subtraction

$$\begin{array}{r} 36 \\ -12 \\ \hline 4 \end{array}$$

First, subtract the ones. Then subtract the tens.

$$\begin{array}{r} 36 \\ -12 \\ \hline 24 \end{array}$$

Subtract.

1.
$$\begin{array}{r} 40 \\ -10 \end{array}$$
$$\begin{array}{r} 80 \\ -30 \end{array}$$
$$\begin{array}{r} 50 \\ -20 \end{array}$$
$$\begin{array}{r} 90 \\ -40 \end{array}$$
$$\begin{array}{r} 85 \\ -10 \end{array}$$
$$\begin{array}{r} 65 \\ -15 \end{array}$$

2.
$$\begin{array}{r} 38 \\ -24 \end{array}$$
$$\begin{array}{r} 69 \\ -45 \end{array}$$
$$\begin{array}{r} 82 \\ -31 \end{array}$$
$$\begin{array}{r} 23 \\ -11 \end{array}$$
$$\begin{array}{r} 97 \\ -72 \end{array}$$
$$\begin{array}{r} 56 \\ -34 \end{array}$$

3.
$$\begin{array}{r} 54 \\ -14 \end{array}$$
$$\begin{array}{r} 77 \\ -51 \end{array}$$
$$\begin{array}{r} 29 \\ -12 \end{array}$$
$$\begin{array}{r} 45 \\ -13 \end{array}$$
$$\begin{array}{r} 57 \\ -24 \end{array}$$
$$\begin{array}{r} 36 \\ -21 \end{array}$$

4.
$$\begin{array}{r} 48 \\ -24 \end{array}$$
$$\begin{array}{r} 39 \\ -17 \end{array}$$
$$\begin{array}{r} 91 \\ -10 \end{array}$$
$$\begin{array}{r} 65 \\ -43 \end{array}$$
$$\begin{array}{r} 73 \\ -31 \end{array}$$
$$\begin{array}{r} 28 \\ -12 \end{array}$$

5.
$$\begin{array}{r} 55 \\ -23 \end{array}$$
$$\begin{array}{r} 47 \\ -21 \end{array}$$
$$\begin{array}{r} 84 \\ -22 \end{array}$$
$$\begin{array}{r} 29 \\ -17 \end{array}$$
$$\begin{array}{r} 99 \\ -33 \end{array}$$
$$\begin{array}{r} 74 \\ -32 \end{array}$$

6.
$$\begin{array}{r} 36 \\ -12 \end{array}$$
$$\begin{array}{r} 58 \\ -46 \end{array}$$
$$\begin{array}{r} 73 \\ -53 \end{array}$$
$$\begin{array}{r} 98 \\ -46 \end{array}$$
$$\begin{array}{r} 53 \\ -41 \end{array}$$
$$\begin{array}{r} 88 \\ -35 \end{array}$$

7.
$$\begin{array}{r} 32 \\ -11 \end{array}$$
$$\begin{array}{r} 68 \\ -33 \end{array}$$
$$\begin{array}{r} 49 \\ -28 \end{array}$$
$$\begin{array}{r} 36 \\ -24 \end{array}$$
$$\begin{array}{r} 96 \\ -43 \end{array}$$
$$\begin{array}{r} 47 \\ -15 \end{array}$$

Subtraction: Regrouping (II)

Name_____ Date_____

```
  2 16
  3̶6̶
- 1 9
    7
```

First, regroup the tens and ones,
borrowing one ten for the ones place.
Subtract the ones.
Then subtract the tens.

```
  2 16
  3̶6̶
- 1 9
   17
```

Subtract.

1.
```
  56        38        50        84        93        73
- 17      - 19      - 25      - 39      - 26      - 26
```

2.
```
  77        47        94        90        65        52
- 59      - 18      - 67      - 43      - 56      - 19
```

3.
```
  80        67        26        37        85        75
- 34      - 28      - 17      - 18      - 57      - 27
```

4.
```
  74        47        92        73        25        44
- 18      - 29      - 63      - 58      - 18      - 36
```

5.
```
  23        94        76        35        50        93
- 15      - 56      - 38      - 19      - 34      - 39
```

6.
```
  40        75        53        92        41        86
- 23      - 58      - 15      - 25      - 26      - 37
```

7.
```
  71        56        50        46        33        71
- 29      - 27      - 23      - 39      - 18      - 53
```

Addition and Subtraction Word Problems

Name_____ Date_____

Read each problem and write an equation to solve it.
Circle **A** if the problem required addition or **S** if it required subtraction.

1. On Monday, Lisa ran a 200-yard dash in seventy-two seconds. Friday, she ran it in sixty-four seconds. How many seconds did she shave off her time?

2. On Tuesday, Kevin did thirty-four jumping jacks. Thursday, he did forty-two. How many jumping jacks did he do in all?

3. On Monday, the swim team swam thirty-five practice laps. Wednesday, they swam forty-two. How many laps did they swim in all?

4. Kelly missed twelve of the thirty-six cheerleading practices. How many practices did she attend?

5. Fourteen members of the thirty-two member gymnastics team are ready to compete on the parallel bars. How many are not?

6. Jordan practiced diving for thirty-five minutes on Thursday and for forty-five minutes on Friday. How many minutes did he practice in all?

7. Of the eighty-two points scored by the basketball team, fifty-four were scored by Peter. How many points did other team members score?

Adding Ones, Tens, and Hundreds

Name_____ Date_____

$$\begin{array}{r} \overset{1}{8}6 \\ +\ 25 \\ \hline 1 \end{array}$$ First add the ones. Regroup the ten.

$$\begin{array}{r} \overset{11}{8}6 \\ +\ 25 \\ \hline 11 \end{array}$$ Then add the tens. Regroup the hundred.

$$\begin{array}{r} \overset{11}{8}6 \\ +\ 25 \\ \hline 111 \end{array}$$ Finally, add the hundreds.

Add.

1.	90 + 20	40 + 60	80 + 60	68 + 40	49 + 54	75 + 52
2.	45 + 65	28 + 83	55 + 60	94 + 27	43 + 69	65 + 87
3.	56 + 75	49 + 86	74 + 79	46 + 99	51 + 49	44 + 57

Add.

4.	135 + 23 158	110 + 50	180 + 11	142 + 37	132 + 26	112 + 45
5.	142 + 36	103 + 92	167 + 21	135 + 14	124 + 52	172 + 16
6.	250 + 37	206 + 23	224 + 51	235 + 43	350 + 32	321 + 67

Addition Practice (II)

Name_____ Date_____

Add.

1.	384 + 15	473 + 26	532 + 56	650 + 25	284 + 14	452 + 31

2.	731 + 37	505 + 30	623 + 42	711 + 68	283 + 12	934 + 51

3.	442 + 57	265 + 21	722 + 67	529 + 40	433 + 54	916 + 82

4.	120 10 + 30	200 40 + 20	720 30 + 40	501 60 + 10	325 15 + 40	915 45 + 30

5.	444 22 + 1	333 55 + 10	635 25 + 15	541 23 + 32	151 14 + 33	832 25 + 12

6.	371 14 + 12	104 72 + 21	232 24 + 21	154 13 + 32	613 52 + 21	803 61 + 25

Addition: Regrouping (III)

Name_____ Date_____

$$\begin{array}{r}\overset{1}{5}86\\+\ 54\\\hline 0\end{array}$$ First, add the ones. Regroup the ten.

$$\begin{array}{r}\overset{11}{5}86\\+\ 54\\\hline 40\end{array}$$ Then add the tens. Regroup the hundred.

$$\begin{array}{r}\overset{11}{5}86\\+\ 54\\\hline 640\end{array}$$ Finally, add the hundreds.

Add.

1.
$$\begin{array}{r}735\\+\ 65\end{array}\qquad\begin{array}{r}545\\+\ 85\end{array}\qquad\begin{array}{r}670\\+\ 95\end{array}\qquad\begin{array}{r}207\\+\ 94\end{array}\qquad\begin{array}{r}248\\+\ 67\end{array}\qquad\begin{array}{r}964\\+\ 29\end{array}$$

2.
$$\begin{array}{r}642\\+\ 78\end{array}\qquad\begin{array}{r}402\\+\ 99\end{array}\qquad\begin{array}{r}294\\+\ 18\end{array}\qquad\begin{array}{r}375\\+\ 26\end{array}\qquad\begin{array}{r}558\\+\ 23\end{array}\qquad\begin{array}{r}137\\+\ 68\end{array}$$

3.
$$\begin{array}{r}271\\+\ 57\end{array}\qquad\begin{array}{r}826\\+\ 77\end{array}\qquad\begin{array}{r}688\\+\ 97\end{array}\qquad\begin{array}{r}509\\+\ 93\end{array}\qquad\begin{array}{r}484\\+\ 26\end{array}\qquad\begin{array}{r}789\\+\ 34\end{array}$$

4.
$$\begin{array}{r}467\\+\ 58\end{array}\qquad\begin{array}{r}933\\+\ 58\end{array}\qquad\begin{array}{r}265\\+\ 93\end{array}\qquad\begin{array}{r}392\\+\ 47\end{array}\qquad\begin{array}{r}255\\+\ 69\end{array}\qquad\begin{array}{r}374\\+\ 97\end{array}$$

5.
$$\begin{array}{r}852\\+\ 53\end{array}\qquad\begin{array}{r}280\\+\ 59\end{array}\qquad\begin{array}{r}476\\+\ 31\end{array}\qquad\begin{array}{r}548\\+\ 63\end{array}\qquad\begin{array}{r}351\\+\ 66\end{array}\qquad\begin{array}{r}405\\+\ 97\end{array}$$

6.
$$\begin{array}{r}233\\+\ 94\end{array}\qquad\begin{array}{r}835\\+\ 58\end{array}\qquad\begin{array}{r}195\\+\ 27\end{array}\qquad\begin{array}{r}604\\+\ 89\end{array}\qquad\begin{array}{r}434\\+\ 96\end{array}\qquad\begin{array}{r}219\\+\ 69\end{array}$$

7.
$$\begin{array}{r}945\\+\ 27\end{array}\qquad\begin{array}{r}513\\+\ 92\end{array}\qquad\begin{array}{r}385\\+\ 43\end{array}\qquad\begin{array}{r}752\\+\ 64\end{array}\qquad\begin{array}{r}133\\+\ 78\end{array}\qquad\begin{array}{r}488\\+\ 76\end{array}$$

Name_____ Date_____

Add.

1. 835   596   294   841   630   398
   + 65   + 23   + 17   + 59   + 81   + 67

2. 590   285   492   137   653   459
     50   30   20   21   22   57
   + 20   + 45   + 19   + 62   + 48   + 26

3. 295   703   331   936   843   582
     39   48   55   12   89   61
   + 42   + 89   + 47   + 26   + 29   + 17

Read each problem then write an equation to solve it.

4. A train has two hundred thirty-two red leather seats and eighty-seven blue leather seats. How many seats are there in all?

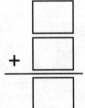

5. The train travels five hundred ten miles to Mainville, then nintey-two miles to Anytown. How many miles does it travel in all?

6. The train carried one hundred sixty-four adults and forty-eight children to Mainville. How many people went to Mainville?

Subtracting Ones, Tens, and Hundreds

Name_____ Date_____

286	First subtract	286	Then subtract	286	Finally, subtract
− 32	the ones.	− 32	the tens.	− 32	the hundreds.
4		54		254	

Subtract.

1.	350 − 20	930 − 10	260 − 50	380 − 40	744 − 20	876 − 30
2.	545 − 31	858 − 43	167 − 54	392 − 81	945 − 12	649 − 28
3.	856 − 45	397 − 73	186 − 35	655 − 15	493 − 62	229 − 23
4.	357 − 24	936 − 12	464 − 51	785 − 72	543 − 13	597 − 56
5.	281 − 31	596 − 45	399 − 73	672 − 61	758 − 38	168 − 46
6.	227 − 15	884 − 21	596 − 24	384 − 12	298 − 47	852 − 21
7.	497 − 53	188 − 44	493 − 32	527 − 13	316 − 11	689 − 42

Subtraction Regrouping (III)

Name_____ Date_____

$$\begin{array}{r} {}^{1}\overset{16}{\cancel{2}\cancel{2}\cancel{6}} \\ -\ 37 \\ \hline 9 \end{array}$$ First subtract the ones. Regroup the ten.

$$\begin{array}{r} {}^{1\ 11}\overset{16}{\cancel{2}\cancel{2}\cancel{6}} \\ -\ 37 \\ \hline 89 \end{array}$$ Then subtract the tens. Regroup the hundred.

$$\begin{array}{r} {}^{1\ 11}\ {}^{1\ 16}\ \overset{}{\cancel{2}\cancel{2}\cancel{6}} \\ -\ 37 \\ \hline 189 \end{array}$$ Finally, subtract the hundreds.

Subtract.

1.
417 − 19   743 − 35   952 − 33   376 − 82   931 − 54   628 − 75

2.
875 − 95   291 − 93   440 − 67   764 − 79   563 − 18   365 − 98

3.
203 − 15   700 − 61   490 − 95   572 − 84   134 − 76   857 − 49

4.
937 − 58   281 − 77   334 − 67   801 − 49   500 − 37   253 − 68

5.
773 − 85   460 − 75   108 − 36   622 − 57   392 − 99   550 − 72

6.
539 − 52   212 − 46   725 − 77   710 − 59   483 − 95   800 − 78

7.
490 − 37   702 − 86   343 − 87   630 − 48   300 − 63   412 − 54

Subtraction Practice (II)

Name_____ Date_____

Subtract.

1.   700   243   904   338   560   600
     − 39   − 67   − 28   − 79   − 47   − 84

2.   302   115   283   408   314   530
     − 68   − 46   − 96   − 55   − 46   − 67

3.   942   200   505   254   109   225
     − 88   − 32   − 17   − 69   − 58   − 69

Read each problem then write an equation to solve it.

4. Of the one hundred thirty-seven students in first grade, seventy-three are boys. How many are girls?

5. Of the two hundred forty-two students in third grade, nintey-three play sports after school. How many do not play sports after school?

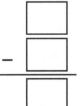
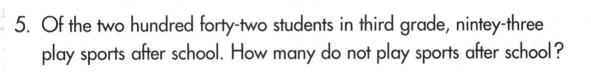

6. Of the seven hundred two students in the primary school, eighty-four have red backpacks. How many do not have red backpacks?

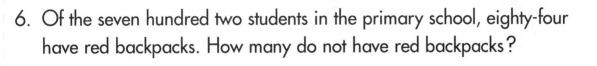
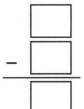

7. Of the five hundred twenty-six students who take a bus to school, nintey-seven sit in front seats. How many do not sit in front seats?

Addition and Subtraction Review

Name_____ Date_____

Solve each problem then fill in the circle next to the correct answer.

1.
```
  370
+  59
```
- a) 419
- b) 329
- c) 429
- d) 319

```
  265
+  46
```
- a) 311
- b) 301
- c) 201
- d) 211

```
  631
+  89
```
- a) 712
- b) 620
- c) 710
- d) 720

2.
```
  729
+  87
```
- a) 816
- b) 817
- c) 706
- d) 806

```
  465
+  58
```
- a) 522
- b) 513
- c) 512
- d) 523

```
  293
+  39
```
- a) 331
- b) 332
- c) 232
- d) 231

3.
```
  345
   36
+  29
```
- a) 310
- b) 411
- c) 410
- d) 401

```
  418
   97
+  63
```
- a) 578
- b) 588
- c) 577
- d) 587

```
  824
   68
+  53
```
- a) 845
- b) 935
- c) 946
- d) 945

Subtract.

4.
```
  634
-  49
```
- a) 595
- b) 586
- c) 585
- d) 695

```
  493
-  85
```
- a) 407
- b) 408
- c) 404
- d) 406

```
  800
-  24
```
- a) 776
- b) 783
- c) 766
- d) 786

5.
```
  114
-  55
```
- a) 56
- b) 58
- c) 57
- d) 59

```
  652
-  89
```
- a) 663
- b) 563
- c) 562
- d) 662

```
  301
-  58
```
- a) 253
- b) 254
- c) 244
- d) 243

6.
```
  934
-  57
```
- a) 874
- b) 877
- c) 887
- b) 875

```
  562
-  95
```
- a) 467
- b) 476
- c) 466
- d) 477

```
  604
-  47
```
- a) 558
- b) 567
- c) 547
- d) 557

Place Value (1)

Name_____ Date_____

Look at the value of each digit in the number 7,462.

Thousands	Hundreds	Tens	Ones
7	4	6	2
7 thousands or 7,000	4 hundreds or 400	6 tens or 60	2 ones or 2

Write the value of each underlined digit.

1. 2,903   7,474   5,683   4,048   6,254

    2000   _____   _____   _____   _____

2. 7,383   9,857   3,584   1,386   4,192

    _____   _____   _____   _____   _____

3. 1,485   6,380   3,095   5,100   8,329

    _____   _____   _____   _____   _____

4. 7,329   2,156   8,040   6,868   4,355

    _____   _____   _____   _____   _____

---

5. Write the digit in the tens place.

1,483__8__   3,490_____

2,661_____   9,955_____

6. Write the digit in the thousands place.

2,293_____   8,115_____

6,804_____   3,776_____

---

7. Write the digit in the hundreds place.

5,003_____   7,284_____

1,979_____   2,865_____

8. Write the digit in the ones place.

4,313_____   3,000_____

9,984_____   6,017_____

Place Value (II)

Name_____ Date_____

Look at the value of each digit in the number 29,546.

Ten Thousands	Thousands	Hundreds	Tens	Ones
2	9	5	4	6
2 ten thousands or 20,000	9 thousands or 9,000	5 hundreds or 500	4 tens or 40	6 ones or 6

Write the value of each underlined digit.

1. 3_4_,906   98,_3_82   10,78_5_   _2_5,944   80,8_2_4

_____   _____   _____   _____   _____

2. 1_6_,328   78,_9_93   46,7_3_1   _1_5,673   62,55_0_

_____   _____   _____   _____   _____

3. _2_9,632   8_1_,555   67,8_3_9   33,_1_50   _5_0,107

_____   _____   _____   _____   _____

Write the digit that is in the specified place value.

4. Tens place in 25,837____

5. Ones place in 76,003 ____

6. Ten thousands place in 67,396 ____

7. Tens place in 14,787____

8. Hundreds place in 16,558 ____

9. Thousands place in 17,210 ____

10. If the 6 in 14,563 was changed to 9, by how much would the value change? _____

11. If the 4 in 47,502 was changed to 7, by how much would the value change? _____

12. If the 9 in 29,564 was changed to 2, by how much would the value change? _____

Rounding

Name_____ Date_____

To round a number to a place value, look at the digit to the right of the given place.

If the digit to the right is 4 or less, round **down** in the given place.

If the digit to the right is 5 or more, round **up** in the given place.

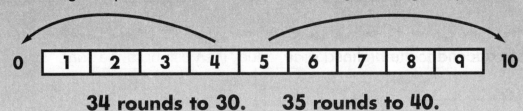

34 rounds to 30.   **35 rounds to 40.**

Round each number to the tens place.

1. 57 _60_   83 _____   75 _____   22 _____   39 _____

2. 64 _____   45 _____   36 _____   53 _____   78 _____

3. 29 _____   31 _____   84 _____   65 _____   92 _____

Round each number to the hundreds place.

4. 284 _300_   765 _____   143 _____   937 _____   498 _____

5. 522 _____   608 _____   181 _____   875 _____   751 _____

6. 396 _____   412 _____   252 _____   749 _____   536 _____

Round each number to the underlined place value.

7. 3̲87 _____   44̲5 _____   2̲91 _____   80̲3 _____   52̲8 _____

8. 6̲40 _____   8̲53 _____   76̲9 _____   13̲4 _____   2̲18 _____

Estimation

Name_____ Date_____

To estimate the sum of 64 + 28, round each addend.

$$64 \longrightarrow 60$$
$$+\ 28 \longrightarrow +\ 30$$
$$\overline{}\quad\overline{90}$$

To estimate the difference of 89 – 42, round the minuend and subtrahend.

$$89 \longrightarrow 90$$
$$-\ 42 \longrightarrow -\ 40$$
$$\overline{}\quad\overline{50}$$

Round each addend to the highest place value, then estimate the sum.

1.
$$\begin{array}{r} 19 \\ +\ 42 \end{array}$$
+ [20] / [40] / [60]

$$\begin{array}{r} 37 \\ +\ 34 \end{array}$$
+ ☐ / ☐ / ☐

$$\begin{array}{r} 84 \\ +\ 67 \end{array}$$
+ ☐ / ☐ / ☐

$$\begin{array}{r} 28 \\ +\ 54 \end{array}$$
+ ☐ / ☐ / ☐

2.
$$\begin{array}{r} 674 \\ +\ 16 \end{array}$$
+ ☐ / ☐ / ☐

$$\begin{array}{r} 432 \\ +\ 59 \end{array}$$
+ ☐ / ☐ / ☐

$$\begin{array}{r} 830 \\ +\ 45 \end{array}$$
+ ☐ / ☐ / ☐

$$\begin{array}{r} 118 \\ +\ 46 \end{array}$$
+ ☐ / ☐ / ☐

Round each minuend and subtrahend to the highest place value, then estimate the difference.

3.
$$\begin{array}{r} 63 \\ -\ 45 \end{array}$$
– ☐ / ☐ / ☐

$$\begin{array}{r} 89 \\ -\ 24 \end{array}$$
– ☐ / ☐ / ☐

$$\begin{array}{r} 42 \\ -45 \end{array}$$
– ☐ / ☐ / ☐

$$\begin{array}{r} 37 \\ -24 \end{array}$$
– ☐ / ☐ / ☐

4.
$$\begin{array}{r} 736 \\ -\ 87 \end{array}$$
– ☐ / ☐ / ☐

$$\begin{array}{r} 487 \\ -\ 64 \end{array}$$
– ☐ / ☐ / ☐

$$\begin{array}{r} 703 \\ -\ 39 \end{array}$$
– ☐ / ☐ / ☐

$$\begin{array}{r} 350 \\ -\ 12 \end{array}$$
– ☐ / ☐ / ☐

5. Jan had 59 marbles. She then won 36 marbles from Alex and 22 from Sam. Estimate how many marbles Jan has now.

☐
☐
+ ☐
☐

Comparing and Ordering Numbers

Name_____ Date_____

| 1,484 > 1,273 | 118 < 244 | 456 = 456 |
| **greater than** | **less than** | **equal to** |

Write **>**, **<**, or **=** to compare each pair of numbers.

1. 74 ___ 76   958 ___ 968   527 ___ 523   1,116 ___ 1,616

2. 8,480 ___ 8,485   7,154 ___ 7,154   2,384 ___ 2,843   5,275 ___ 5,265

3. 3,772 ___ 3,327   6,114 ___ 6,414   4,305 ___ 4,350   9,329 ___ 9,239

Write a number to complete each number sentence correctly.

4.   23 < _____ < 28   200 > _____ > 175   1,122 < _____ < 1,222

5.   378 < _____ < 389   5,367 > _____ > 5,342   8,946 > _____ > 8,921

Rewrite each set of numbers in order from greatest to least.

6. 167, 176, 165, 156, 175 _____ > _____ > _____ > _____ > _____

7. 1,212, 1,112, 1,211, 1,121, 1,222 _____ > _____ > _____ > _____ > _____

Rewrite each set of numbers in order from least to greatest.

8. 323, 233, 232, 322, 333 _____ < _____ < _____ < _____ < _____

9. 6,414, 6,411, 6,114, 6,141, 6,441 _____ < _____ < _____ < _____ < _____

Number Patterns

Name_____ Date_____

Number Pattern	Rule	Proof
0, 2, 4, 6, 8, 10	Add 2 or + 2	**0** + 2 = **2** + 2 = **4** + 2 = **6** + 2 = **8** + 2 = **10**
90, 80, 70, 60, 50	Subtract 10 or − 10	**90** − 10 = **80** − 10 = **70** − 10 = **60** − 10 = **50**

Write the next number in each pattern. Then write the rule for the pattern.

1. 5, 10, 15, 20, 25, __30__   Rule: __Add 5 (or) + 5__

2. 3, 6, 9, 12, 15, _____   Rule: _____

3. 36, 30, 24, 18, 12, _____   Rule: _____

4. 7, 14, 21, 28, 35, _____   Rule: _____

5. 20, 16, 12, 8, 4, _____   Rule: _____

6. 6, 12, 18, 24, 30, _____   Rule: _____

Continue each pattern according to its rule.

7. Rule: Add 9   __0__ , __9__ , ____ , ____ , ____ , ____

8. Rule: Subtract 3   __27__ , __24__ , ____ , ____ , ____ , ____

9. Rule: Add 8   __0__ , ____ , ____ , ____ , ____ , ____

Multiplication Terms

Name_____ Date_____

Multiplication is a faster way of adding the same number a given amount of times.

$4 + 4 + 4 = 4$ added 3 times $= 4 \times 3$

Numbers being multiplied are called **factors**. The answer is the **product**.

4	x	3	=	12
factor		**factor**		**product**

Write the sum in the box. Write how many times you added in the circle. Then rewrite those numbers to complete the multiplication equation.

1. $2 + 2 + 2 + 2 + 2 =$ ⬜ 10

   How many times did you add 2? ⑤ times
   ⑤ $\times 2 =$ ⬜ 10

2. $1 + 1 + 1 + 1 + 1 + 1 + 1 =$ ⬜

   How many times did you add 1? ◯ times
   ◯ $\times 1 =$ ⬜

3. $5 + 5 + 5 =$ ⬜

   How many times did you add 5? ◯ times
   ◯ $\times 5 =$ ⬜

4. $3 + 3 + 3 + 3 + 3 + 3 =$ ⬜

   How many times did you add 3? ◯ times
   ◯ $\times 3 =$ ⬜

5. $8 + 8 =$ ⬜

   How many times did you add 8? ◯ times
   ◯ $\times 8 =$ ⬜

6. $7 + 7 + 7 + 7 =$ ⬜

   How many times did you add 7? ◯ times
   ◯ $\times 7 =$ ⬜

7. $6 + 6 + 6 + 6 + 6 =$ ⬜

   How many times did you add 6? ◯ times
   ◯ $\times 6 =$ ⬜

Multiplication Facts (I)

Name_____ Date_____

Any number multiplied by zero equals zero. Zero multiplied by any other number will also equal zero.

$3 \times 0 = 0$ added 3 times $= 0 + 0 + 0 = 0$
$0 \times 3 = 3$ added 0 times $= 0$

A number multiplied by one equals itself. One multiplied by any other number equals that number.

$3 \times 1 = 3$ added 1 time $= 3$
$1 \times 3 = 1$ added 3 times $= 1 + 1 + 1 = 3$

Multiply.

1.
$\begin{array}{r} 0 \\ \times\ 4 \\ \hline \end{array}$
$\begin{array}{r} 1 \\ \times\ 5 \\ \hline \end{array}$
$\begin{array}{r} 9 \\ \times\ 1 \\ \hline \end{array}$
$\begin{array}{r} 7 \\ \times\ 0 \\ \hline \end{array}$
$\begin{array}{r} 5 \\ \times\ 0 \\ \hline \end{array}$
$\begin{array}{r} 1 \\ \times\ 1 \\ \hline \end{array}$

2.
$\begin{array}{r} 7 \\ \times\ 1 \\ \hline \end{array}$
$\begin{array}{r} 3 \\ \times\ 0 \\ \hline \end{array}$
$\begin{array}{r} 6 \\ \times\ 1 \\ \hline \end{array}$
$\begin{array}{r} 1 \\ \times\ 8 \\ \hline \end{array}$
$\begin{array}{r} 4 \\ \times\ 1 \\ \hline \end{array}$
$\begin{array}{r} 0 \\ \times\ 2 \\ \hline \end{array}$

3.
$\begin{array}{r} 2 \\ \times\ 1 \\ \hline \end{array}$
$\begin{array}{r} 4 \\ \times\ 0 \\ \hline \end{array}$
$\begin{array}{r} 5 \\ \times\ 1 \\ \hline \end{array}$
$\begin{array}{r} 1 \\ \times\ 3 \\ \hline \end{array}$
$\begin{array}{r} 0 \\ \times\ 7 \\ \hline \end{array}$
$\begin{array}{r} 8 \\ \times\ 0 \\ \hline \end{array}$

4.
$\begin{array}{r} 1 \\ \times\ 6 \\ \hline \end{array}$
$\begin{array}{r} 1 \\ \times\ 2 \\ \hline \end{array}$
$\begin{array}{r} 9 \\ \times\ 0 \\ \hline \end{array}$
$\begin{array}{r} 8 \\ \times\ 1 \\ \hline \end{array}$
$\begin{array}{r} 1 \\ \times\ 9 \\ \hline \end{array}$
$\begin{array}{r} 0 \\ \times\ 3 \\ \hline \end{array}$

5.
$\begin{array}{r} 1 \\ \times\ 0 \\ \hline \end{array}$
$\begin{array}{r} 6 \\ \times\ 0 \\ \hline \end{array}$
$\begin{array}{r} 2 \\ \times\ 0 \\ \hline \end{array}$
$\begin{array}{r} 1 \\ \times\ 4 \\ \hline \end{array}$
$\begin{array}{r} 0 \\ \times\ 5 \\ \hline \end{array}$
$\begin{array}{r} 0 \\ \times\ 1 \\ \hline \end{array}$

6.
$\begin{array}{r} 0 \\ \times\ 6 \\ \hline \end{array}$
$\begin{array}{r} 1 \\ \times\ 7 \\ \hline \end{array}$
$\begin{array}{r} 0 \\ \times\ 9 \\ \hline \end{array}$
$\begin{array}{r} 0 \\ \times\ 8 \\ \hline \end{array}$
$\begin{array}{r} 3 \\ \times\ 1 \\ \hline \end{array}$
$\begin{array}{r} 0 \\ \times\ 2 \\ \hline \end{array}$

7. Label each number as a factor or product.

$$1 \qquad \times \qquad 5 \qquad = \qquad 5$$

_____ _____ _____

Multiplication Facts (II)

Name_____ Date_____

1. Count by 2s to complete the chart.

x	0	1	2	3	4	5	6	7	8	9
2	0	2	4							

Multiply.

2.
$$\begin{array}{r} 7 \\ \times\,2 \\ \hline \end{array} \qquad \begin{array}{r} 2 \\ \times\,3 \\ \hline \end{array} \qquad \begin{array}{r} 6 \\ \times\,2 \\ \hline \end{array} \qquad \begin{array}{r} 2 \\ \times\,8 \\ \hline \end{array} \qquad \begin{array}{r} 2 \\ \times\,1 \\ \hline \end{array} \qquad \begin{array}{r} 4 \\ \times\,2 \\ \hline \end{array}$$

3.
$$\begin{array}{r} 0 \\ \times\,2 \\ \hline \end{array} \qquad \begin{array}{r} 3 \\ \times\,1 \\ \hline \end{array} \qquad \begin{array}{r} 2 \\ \times\,9 \\ \hline \end{array} \qquad \begin{array}{r} 3 \\ \times\,2 \\ \hline \end{array} \qquad \begin{array}{r} 7 \\ \times\,1 \\ \hline \end{array} \qquad \begin{array}{r} 8 \\ \times\,2 \\ \hline \end{array}$$

4.
$$\begin{array}{r} 2 \\ \times\,4 \\ \hline \end{array} \qquad \begin{array}{r} 1 \\ \times\,2 \\ \hline \end{array} \qquad \begin{array}{r} 8 \\ \times\,2 \\ \hline \end{array} \qquad \begin{array}{r} 2 \\ \times\,0 \\ \hline \end{array} \qquad \begin{array}{r} 2 \\ \times\,4 \\ \hline \end{array} \qquad \begin{array}{r} 2 \\ \times\,5 \\ \hline \end{array}$$

5.
$$\begin{array}{r} 9 \\ \times\,2 \\ \hline \end{array} \qquad \begin{array}{r} 2 \\ \times\,7 \\ \hline \end{array} \qquad \begin{array}{r} 2 \\ \times\,6 \\ \hline \end{array} \qquad \begin{array}{r} 0 \\ \times\,4 \\ \hline \end{array} \qquad \begin{array}{r} 5 \\ \times\,2 \\ \hline \end{array} \qquad \begin{array}{r} 2 \\ \times\,2 \\ \hline \end{array}$$

Write and solve a multiplication equation for each problem.

6. Anna ate two apples each day for four days.
   How many apples did she eat in all?   _____ x _____ = _____

7. Pete ate two slices of pizza each day for a week.
   How many slices did he eat in all?   _____ x _____ = _____

Multiplication Facts (III)

Name_____ Date_____

1. Count by 3s to complete the chart.

x	0	1	2	3	4	5	6	7	8	9
3	0	3	6							

Multiply.

2.
$$\begin{array}{r} 7 \\ \times\ 3 \\ \hline \end{array}\qquad \begin{array}{r} 3 \\ \times\ 3 \\ \hline \end{array}\qquad \begin{array}{r} 6 \\ \times\ 3 \\ \hline \end{array}\qquad \begin{array}{r} 3 \\ \times\ 8 \\ \hline \end{array}\qquad \begin{array}{r} 3 \\ \times\ 1 \\ \hline \end{array}\qquad \begin{array}{r} 4 \\ \times\ 3 \\ \hline \end{array}$$

3.
$$\begin{array}{r} 0 \\ \times\ 3 \\ \hline \end{array}\qquad \begin{array}{r} 0 \\ \times\ 6 \\ \hline \end{array}\qquad \begin{array}{r} 3 \\ \times\ 9 \\ \hline \end{array}\qquad \begin{array}{r} 2 \\ \times\ 6 \\ \hline \end{array}\qquad \begin{array}{r} 1 \\ \times\ 7 \\ \hline \end{array}\qquad \begin{array}{r} 8 \\ \times\ 3 \\ \hline \end{array}$$

4.
$$\begin{array}{r} 3 \\ \times\ 4 \\ \hline \end{array}\qquad \begin{array}{r} 1 \\ \times\ 3 \\ \hline \end{array}\qquad \begin{array}{r} 8 \\ \times\ 3 \\ \hline \end{array}\qquad \begin{array}{r} 3 \\ \times\ 0 \\ \hline \end{array}\qquad \begin{array}{r} 2 \\ \times\ 4 \\ \hline \end{array}\qquad \begin{array}{r} 3 \\ \times\ 5 \\ \hline \end{array}$$

5.
$$\begin{array}{r} 9 \\ \times\ 3 \\ \hline \end{array}\qquad \begin{array}{r} 3 \\ \times\ 7 \\ \hline \end{array}\qquad \begin{array}{r} 3 \\ \times\ 6 \\ \hline \end{array}\qquad \begin{array}{r} 8 \\ \times\ 1 \\ \hline \end{array}\qquad \begin{array}{r} 5 \\ \times\ 3 \\ \hline \end{array}\qquad \begin{array}{r} 0 \\ \times\ 4 \\ \hline \end{array}$$

Write and solve a multiplication equation for each problem.

6. At the market, oranges are priced three for one
   dollar. How many oranges does four dollars buy?   ____ x ____ = ____

7. Tomatoes are sold in packages of three.
   How many tomatoes are in eight packages?   ____ x ____ = ____

Multiplication Facts (IV)

Name_____ Date_____

1. Count by 4s to complete the chart.

x	0	1	2	3	4	5	6	7	8	9
4	0	4	8							

Multiply.

2.
$$\begin{array}{r} 0 \\ \times\ 4 \\ \hline \end{array}$$
$$\begin{array}{r} 1 \\ \times\ 7 \\ \hline \end{array}$$
$$\begin{array}{r} 4 \\ \times\ 9 \\ \hline \end{array}$$
$$\begin{array}{r} 4 \\ \times\ 2 \\ \hline \end{array}$$
$$\begin{array}{r} 3 \\ \times\ 4 \\ \hline \end{array}$$
$$\begin{array}{r} 8 \\ \times\ 4 \\ \hline \end{array}$$

3.
$$\begin{array}{r} 7 \\ \times\ 4 \\ \hline \end{array}$$
$$\begin{array}{r} 4 \\ \times\ 4 \\ \hline \end{array}$$
$$\begin{array}{r} 6 \\ \times\ 4 \\ \hline \end{array}$$
$$\begin{array}{r} 4 \\ \times\ 8 \\ \hline \end{array}$$
$$\begin{array}{r} 4 \\ \times\ 1 \\ \hline \end{array}$$
$$\begin{array}{r} 4 \\ \times\ 5 \\ \hline \end{array}$$

4.
$$\begin{array}{r} 2 \\ \times\ 6 \\ \hline \end{array}$$
$$\begin{array}{r} 4 \\ \times\ 7 \\ \hline \end{array}$$
$$\begin{array}{r} 4 \\ \times\ 0 \\ \hline \end{array}$$
$$\begin{array}{r} 1 \\ \times\ 8 \\ \hline \end{array}$$
$$\begin{array}{r} 5 \\ \times\ 4 \\ \hline \end{array}$$
$$\begin{array}{r} 9 \\ \times\ 4 \\ \hline \end{array}$$

5.
$$\begin{array}{r} 4 \\ \times\ 3 \\ \hline \end{array}$$
$$\begin{array}{r} 1 \\ \times\ 4 \\ \hline \end{array}$$
$$\begin{array}{r} 3 \\ \times\ 7 \\ \hline \end{array}$$
$$\begin{array}{r} 4 \\ \times\ 6 \\ \hline \end{array}$$
$$\begin{array}{r} 2 \\ \times\ 4 \\ \hline \end{array}$$
$$\begin{array}{r} 2 \\ \times\ 8 \\ \hline \end{array}$$

Write and solve a multiplication equation for each problem.

6. Mrs. Smith baked four apple pies. She cut each pie
   into eight pieces. How many pieces did she have in all?   ____ x ____ = ____

7. Mrs. Cary baked four chocolate cakes and cut each one
   into nine pieces. How many pieces did she have in all?   ____ x ____ = ____

Name_____ Date_____

1. Count by 5s to complete the chart.

x	0	1	2	3	4	5	6	7	8	9
5	0	5	10							

Multiply.

2.
$$9 \times 5$$
$$5 \times 7$$
$$5 \times 0$$
$$1 \times 6$$
$$4 \times 0$$
$$3 \times 7$$

3.
$$0 \times 5$$
$$3 \times 1$$
$$5 \times 9$$
$$5 \times 2$$
$$3 \times 5$$
$$8 \times 5$$

4.
$$7 \times 5$$
$$4 \times 5$$
$$6 \times 5$$
$$5 \times 8$$
$$5 \times 1$$
$$5 \times 5$$

5.
$$5 \times 3$$
$$1 \times 5$$
$$4 \times 9$$
$$5 \times 6$$
$$2 \times 5$$
$$5 \times 4$$

Write and solve a multiplication equation for each problem.

6. Jeremy bought six pieces of gum. Each piece cost
five cents. How many cents did Jeremy spend in all?   _____ x _____ = _____

7. Alyssa bought nine pieces of gum at the same price.
How many cents did she spend in all?   _____ x _____ = _____

Multiplication Review

Name_____ Date_____

1. Complete the multiplication chart.

x	0	1	2	3	4	5	6	7	8	9
0	0							0		
1		1							8	
2				6	10					
3		6						21		
4		4		16						
5		5						35		

Find the missing factor.

2. $2 \times \underline{\quad} = 10$ $\qquad$ $3 \times \underline{\quad} = 18$ $\qquad$ $\underline{\quad} \times 4 = 0$ $\qquad$ $5 \times \underline{\quad} = 45$

3. $\underline{\quad} \times 8 = 16$ $\qquad$ $1 \times \underline{\quad} = 9$ $\qquad$ $\underline{\quad} \times 7 = 35$ $\qquad$ $\underline{\quad} \times 8 = 32$

4. $4 \times \underline{\quad} = 28$ $\qquad$ $\underline{\quad} \times 6 = 12$ $\qquad$ $5 \times \underline{\quad} = 20$ $\qquad$ $3 \times \underline{\quad} = 27$

5. $\underline{\quad} \times 5 = 5$ $\qquad$ $\underline{\quad} \times 3 = 9$ $\qquad$ $4 \times \underline{\quad} = 24$ $\qquad$ $5 \times \underline{\quad} = 15$

Multiplication Facts Drill (1)

Name_____ Date_____

Multiply.

1.
$$\begin{array}{r}4\\ \times\,5\\ \hline\end{array}\qquad \begin{array}{r}3\\ \times\,7\\ \hline\end{array}\qquad \begin{array}{r}4\\ \times\,0\\ \hline\end{array}\qquad \begin{array}{r}1\\ \times\,1\\ \hline\end{array}\qquad \begin{array}{r}3\\ \times\,3\\ \hline\end{array}\qquad \begin{array}{r}2\\ \times\,6\\ \hline\end{array}$$

2.
$$\begin{array}{r}7\\ \times\,1\\ \hline\end{array}\qquad \begin{array}{r}3\\ \times\,0\\ \hline\end{array}\qquad \begin{array}{r}2\\ \times\,9\\ \hline\end{array}\qquad \begin{array}{r}3\\ \times\,2\\ \hline\end{array}\qquad \begin{array}{r}1\\ \times\,4\\ \hline\end{array}\qquad \begin{array}{r}3\\ \times\,5\\ \hline\end{array}$$

3.
$$\begin{array}{r}1\\ \times\,5\\ \hline\end{array}\qquad \begin{array}{r}2\\ \times\,3\\ \hline\end{array}\qquad \begin{array}{r}1\\ \times\,2\\ \hline\end{array}\qquad \begin{array}{r}3\\ \times\,8\\ \hline\end{array}\qquad \begin{array}{r}0\\ \times\,1\\ \hline\end{array}\qquad \begin{array}{r}4\\ \times\,3\\ \hline\end{array}$$

4.
$$\begin{array}{r}1\\ \times\,3\\ \hline\end{array}\qquad \begin{array}{r}2\\ \times\,7\\ \hline\end{array}\qquad \begin{array}{r}5\\ \times\,3\\ \hline\end{array}\qquad \begin{array}{r}8\\ \times\,2\\ \hline\end{array}\qquad \begin{array}{r}3\\ \times\,6\\ \hline\end{array}\qquad \begin{array}{r}4\\ \times\,4\\ \hline\end{array}$$

5.
$$\begin{array}{r}4\\ \times\,6\\ \hline\end{array}\qquad \begin{array}{r}4\\ \times\,7\\ \hline\end{array}\qquad \begin{array}{r}2\\ \times\,0\\ \hline\end{array}\qquad \begin{array}{r}9\\ \times\,1\\ \hline\end{array}\qquad \begin{array}{r}1\\ \times\,0\\ \hline\end{array}\qquad \begin{array}{r}2\\ \times\,5\\ \hline\end{array}$$

6.
$$\begin{array}{r}5\\ \times\,2\\ \hline\end{array}\qquad \begin{array}{r}2\\ \times\,1\\ \hline\end{array}\qquad \begin{array}{r}3\\ \times\,9\\ \hline\end{array}\qquad \begin{array}{r}1\\ \times\,2\\ \hline\end{array}\qquad \begin{array}{r}7\\ \times\,3\\ \hline\end{array}\qquad \begin{array}{r}5\\ \times\,1\\ \hline\end{array}$$

7.
$$\begin{array}{r}1\\ \times\,8\\ \hline\end{array}\qquad \begin{array}{r}6\\ \times\,3\\ \hline\end{array}\qquad \begin{array}{r}3\\ \times\,1\\ \hline\end{array}\qquad \begin{array}{r}2\\ \times\,8\\ \hline\end{array}\qquad \begin{array}{r}2\\ \times\,2\\ \hline\end{array}\qquad \begin{array}{r}5\\ \times\,7\\ \hline\end{array}$$

8.
$$\begin{array}{r}8\\ \times\,1\\ \hline\end{array}\qquad \begin{array}{r}6\\ \times\,2\\ \hline\end{array}\qquad \begin{array}{r}4\\ \times\,9\\ \hline\end{array}\qquad \begin{array}{r}1\\ \times\,6\\ \hline\end{array}\qquad \begin{array}{r}8\\ \times\,3\\ \hline\end{array}\qquad \begin{array}{r}3\\ \times\,4\\ \hline\end{array}$$

9.
$$\begin{array}{r}5\\ \times\,5\\ \hline\end{array}\qquad \begin{array}{r}1\\ \times\,7\\ \hline\end{array}\qquad \begin{array}{r}9\\ \times\,3\\ \hline\end{array}\qquad \begin{array}{r}4\\ \times\,1\\ \hline\end{array}\qquad \begin{array}{r}0\\ \times\,3\\ \hline\end{array}\qquad \begin{array}{r}7\\ \times\,2\\ \hline\end{array}$$

10.
$$\begin{array}{r}5\\ \times\,4\\ \hline\end{array}\qquad \begin{array}{r}6\\ \times\,1\\ \hline\end{array}\qquad \begin{array}{r}1\\ \times\,9\\ \hline\end{array}\qquad \begin{array}{r}4\\ \times\,2\\ \hline\end{array}\qquad \begin{array}{r}2\\ \times\,4\\ \hline\end{array}\qquad \begin{array}{r}4\\ \times\,8\\ \hline\end{array}$$

Multiplication Facts Drill (II)

Name_____ Date_____

Multiply.

1.
$\begin{array}{r} 1 \\ \times\ 5 \\ \hline \end{array}$
$\begin{array}{r} 2 \\ \times\ 3 \\ \hline \end{array}$
$\begin{array}{r} 7 \\ \times\ 0 \\ \hline \end{array}$
$\begin{array}{r} 8 \\ \times\ 1 \\ \hline \end{array}$
$\begin{array}{r} 9 \\ \times\ 2 \\ \hline \end{array}$
$\begin{array}{r} 6 \\ \times\ 1 \\ \hline \end{array}$

2.
$\begin{array}{r} 3 \\ \times\ 1 \\ \hline \end{array}$
$\begin{array}{r} 7 \\ \times\ 5 \\ \hline \end{array}$
$\begin{array}{r} 4 \\ \times\ 5 \\ \hline \end{array}$
$\begin{array}{r} 9 \\ \times\ 3 \\ \hline \end{array}$
$\begin{array}{r} 7 \\ \times\ 4 \\ \hline \end{array}$
$\begin{array}{r} 6 \\ \times\ 5 \\ \hline \end{array}$

3.
$\begin{array}{r} 2 \\ \times\ 5 \\ \hline \end{array}$
$\begin{array}{r} 8 \\ \times\ 3 \\ \hline \end{array}$
$\begin{array}{r} 5 \\ \times\ 2 \\ \hline \end{array}$
$\begin{array}{r} 3 \\ \times\ 4 \\ \hline \end{array}$
$\begin{array}{r} 2 \\ \times\ 1 \\ \hline \end{array}$
$\begin{array}{r} 5 \\ \times\ 9 \\ \hline \end{array}$

4.
$\begin{array}{r} 6 \\ \times\ 3 \\ \hline \end{array}$
$\begin{array}{r} 2 \\ \times\ 8 \\ \hline \end{array}$
$\begin{array}{r} 4 \\ \times\ 9 \\ \hline \end{array}$
$\begin{array}{r} 1 \\ \times\ 1 \\ \hline \end{array}$
$\begin{array}{r} 9 \\ \times\ 4 \\ \hline \end{array}$
$\begin{array}{r} 4 \\ \times\ 4 \\ \hline \end{array}$

5.
$\begin{array}{r} 5 \\ \times\ 1 \\ \hline \end{array}$
$\begin{array}{r} 3 \\ \times\ 6 \\ \hline \end{array}$
$\begin{array}{r} 2 \\ \times\ 7 \\ \hline \end{array}$
$\begin{array}{r} 5 \\ \times\ 3 \\ \hline \end{array}$
$\begin{array}{r} 8 \\ \times\ 0 \\ \hline \end{array}$
$\begin{array}{r} 3 \\ \times\ 5 \\ \hline \end{array}$

6.
$\begin{array}{r} 3 \\ \times\ 7 \\ \hline \end{array}$
$\begin{array}{r} 1 \\ \times\ 6 \\ \hline \end{array}$
$\begin{array}{r} 6 \\ \times\ 0 \\ \hline \end{array}$
$\begin{array}{r} 2 \\ \times\ 2 \\ \hline \end{array}$
$\begin{array}{r} 1 \\ \times\ 9 \\ \hline \end{array}$
$\begin{array}{r} 4 \\ \times\ 8 \\ \hline \end{array}$

7.
$\begin{array}{r} 1 \\ \times\ 4 \\ \hline \end{array}$
$\begin{array}{r} 2 \\ \times\ 0 \\ \hline \end{array}$
$\begin{array}{r} 3 \\ \times\ 8 \\ \hline \end{array}$
$\begin{array}{r} 6 \\ \times\ 4 \\ \hline \end{array}$
$\begin{array}{r} 7 \\ \times\ 2 \\ \hline \end{array}$
$\begin{array}{r} 5 \\ \times\ 6 \\ \hline \end{array}$

8.
$\begin{array}{r} 8 \\ \times\ 4 \\ \hline \end{array}$
$\begin{array}{r} 2 \\ \times\ 6 \\ \hline \end{array}$
$\begin{array}{r} 1 \\ \times\ 2 \\ \hline \end{array}$
$\begin{array}{r} 4 \\ \times\ 7 \\ \hline \end{array}$
$\begin{array}{r} 2 \\ \times\ 4 \\ \hline \end{array}$
$\begin{array}{r} 1 \\ \times\ 7 \\ \hline \end{array}$

9.
$\begin{array}{r} 4 \\ \times\ 3 \\ \hline \end{array}$
$\begin{array}{r} 7 \\ \times\ 3 \\ \hline \end{array}$
$\begin{array}{r} 4 \\ \times\ 6 \\ \hline \end{array}$
$\begin{array}{r} 3 \\ \times\ 9 \\ \hline \end{array}$
$\begin{array}{r} 5 \\ \times\ 7 \\ \hline \end{array}$
$\begin{array}{r} 9 \\ \times\ 1 \\ \hline \end{array}$

10.
$\begin{array}{r} 6 \\ \times\ 2 \\ \hline \end{array}$
$\begin{array}{r} 5 \\ \times\ 8 \\ \hline \end{array}$
$\begin{array}{r} 9 \\ \times\ 5 \\ \hline \end{array}$
$\begin{array}{r} 8 \\ \times\ 2 \\ \hline \end{array}$
$\begin{array}{r} 0 \\ \times\ 4 \\ \hline \end{array}$
$\begin{array}{r} 2 \\ \times\ 9 \\ \hline \end{array}$

Multiplication Word Problems

Name_____ Date_____

Read each problem then fill in the circle next to the correct equation used to solve it.

1. Angela planted two rows of bean plants in her garden. Each row has nine plants. How many bean plants are there in all?

   ○ a) 2 x 9 = 16   ○ b) 2 x 9 = 18   ○ c) 2 x 9 = 19   ○ d) 2 x 9 = 14

2. Angela planted four rows of carrots. Each row has eight carrots. How many carrots are there in all?

   ○ a) 4 x 8 = 24   ○ b) 4 x 8 = 36   ○ c) 4 x 8 = 32   ○ d) 4 x 8 = 28

3. Angela planted three rows of radish seeds. She hopes to grow six radishes in each row. If she does, how many radishes will Angela have in all?

   ○ a) 3 x 6 = 18   ○ b) 3 x 6 = 12   ○ c) 3 x 6 = 24   ○ d) 3 x 6 = 21

4. Lamar planted five rows of tomatoes in his garden. Each row has four plants. How many tomato plants are there in all?

   ○ a) 5 x 4 = 15   ○ b) 5 x 4 = 25   ○ c) 5 x 4 = 24   ○ d) 5 x 4 = 20

5. Lamar planted four rows of lettuce. Each row has seven lettuce plants. How many lettuce plants are there in all?

   ○ a) 4 x 7 = 27   ○ b) 4 x 7 = 28   ○ c) 4 x 7 = 36   ○ d) 4 x 7 = 32

6. Lamar planted three squash plants. He hopes to harvest nine squashes from each plant. If he does, how many squashes will Lamar have in all?

   ○ a) 3 x 9 = 24   ○ b) 3 x 9 = 18   ○ c) 3 x 9 = 21   ○ d) 3 x 9 = 27

7. Lamar used two rolls of plastic fencing to fence in his garden. Each roll had six yards of fencing. How many yards of fencing did Lamar use in all?

   ○ a) 2 x 6 = 18   ○ b) 2 x 6 = 10   ○ c) 2 x 6 = 12   ○ d) 2 x 6 = 14

8. Lamar tended his garden four times a week. How many times did he tend in six weeks?

   ○ a) 4 x 6 = 24   ○ b) 4 x 6 = 27   ○ c) 4 x 6 = 28   ○ d) 4 x 6 = 26

Addition

$$\begin{array}{r} 586 \\ + 213 \\ \hline 9 \end{array}$$ First add the ones.
$$\begin{array}{r} 586 \\ + 213 \\ \hline 99 \end{array}$$ Then add the tens.
$$\begin{array}{r} 586 \\ + 213 \\ \hline 799 \end{array}$$ Finally, add the hundreds.

Add.

1.
$$\begin{array}{r} 200 \\ + 187 \\ \hline \end{array}$$
$$\begin{array}{r} 600 \\ + 243 \\ \hline \end{array}$$
$$\begin{array}{r} 850 \\ + 125 \\ \hline \end{array}$$
$$\begin{array}{r} 350 \\ + 546 \\ \hline \end{array}$$
$$\begin{array}{r} 410 \\ + 151 \\ \hline \end{array}$$
$$\begin{array}{r} 520 \\ + 334 \\ \hline \end{array}$$

2.
$$\begin{array}{r} 806 \\ + 192 \\ \hline \end{array}$$
$$\begin{array}{r} 374 \\ + 402 \\ \hline \end{array}$$
$$\begin{array}{r} 212 \\ + 673 \\ \hline \end{array}$$
$$\begin{array}{r} 633 \\ + 145 \\ \hline \end{array}$$
$$\begin{array}{r} 741 \\ + 233 \\ \hline \end{array}$$
$$\begin{array}{r} 555 \\ + 231 \\ \hline \end{array}$$

3.
$$\begin{array}{r} 832 \\ + 141 \\ \hline \end{array}$$
$$\begin{array}{r} 284 \\ + 612 \\ \hline \end{array}$$
$$\begin{array}{r} 456 \\ + 232 \\ \hline \end{array}$$
$$\begin{array}{r} 382 \\ + 116 \\ \hline \end{array}$$
$$\begin{array}{r} 137 \\ + 332 \\ \hline \end{array}$$
$$\begin{array}{r} 433 \\ + 541 \\ \hline \end{array}$$

4.
$$\begin{array}{r} 553 \\ + 335 \\ \hline \end{array}$$
$$\begin{array}{r} 109 \\ + 230 \\ \hline \end{array}$$
$$\begin{array}{r} 323 \\ + 452 \\ \hline \end{array}$$
$$\begin{array}{r} 657 \\ + 311 \\ \hline \end{array}$$
$$\begin{array}{r} 392 \\ + 405 \\ \hline \end{array}$$
$$\begin{array}{r} 265 \\ + 314 \\ \hline \end{array}$$

5.
$$\begin{array}{r} 404 \\ + 512 \\ \hline \end{array}$$
$$\begin{array}{r} 118 \\ + 560 \\ \hline \end{array}$$
$$\begin{array}{r} 584 \\ + 413 \\ \hline \end{array}$$
$$\begin{array}{r} 227 \\ + 721 \\ \hline \end{array}$$
$$\begin{array}{r} 443 \\ + 456 \\ \hline \end{array}$$
$$\begin{array}{r} 125 \\ + 502 \\ \hline \end{array}$$

6.
$$\begin{array}{r} 732 \\ + 126 \\ \hline \end{array}$$
$$\begin{array}{r} 252 \\ + 713 \\ \hline \end{array}$$
$$\begin{array}{r} 435 \\ + 164 \\ \hline \end{array}$$
$$\begin{array}{r} 816 \\ + 180 \\ \hline \end{array}$$
$$\begin{array}{r} 554 \\ + 121 \\ \hline \end{array}$$
$$\begin{array}{r} 644 \\ + 352 \\ \hline \end{array}$$

7.
$$\begin{array}{r} 372 \\ + 116 \\ \hline \end{array}$$
$$\begin{array}{r} 121 \\ + 248 \\ \hline \end{array}$$
$$\begin{array}{r} 505 \\ + 381 \\ \hline \end{array}$$
$$\begin{array}{r} 136 \\ + 620 \\ \hline \end{array}$$
$$\begin{array}{r} 258 \\ + 231 \\ \hline \end{array}$$
$$\begin{array}{r} 149 \\ + 730 \\ \hline \end{array}$$

Unit 3

Addition: Regrouping

Name_____ Date_____

$$
\begin{array}{r}
\overset{1}{5}8\mathbf{6} \\
+\ 65\mathbf{4} \\
\hline
\mathbf{0}
\end{array}
\qquad
\begin{array}{r}
\overset{11}{5}8\mathbf{6} \\
+\ 6\mathbf{5}4 \\
\hline
\mathbf{4}0
\end{array}
\qquad
\begin{array}{r}
\overset{111}{\mathbf{5}}86 \\
+\ \mathbf{6}54 \\
\hline
\mathbf{2}40
\end{array}
\qquad
\begin{array}{r}
\overset{1}{5}\overset{11}{8}6 \\
+\ 654 \\
\hline
\mathbf{1},240
\end{array}
$$

First add the ones. Regroup the ten.   Then add the tens. Regroup the hundred.   Then add the hundreds. Regroup the thousand.   Finally, add the thousands.

Add.

1.
$$540 + 697 \qquad 601 + 599 \qquad 956 + 655 \qquad 438 + 566 \qquad 869 + 656 \qquad 557 + 474$$

2.
$$926 + 695 \qquad 694 + 608 \qquad 565 + 678 \qquad 367 + 645 \qquad 756 + 556 \qquad 555 + 846$$

3.
$$946 + 676 \qquad 594 + 615 \qquad 558 + 545 \qquad 495 + 796 \qquad 647 + 485 \qquad 465 + 546$$

4.
$$154 + 947 \qquad 689 + 542 \qquad 458 + 755 \qquad 657 + 466 \qquad 495 + 805 \qquad 569 + 864$$

5.
$$433 + 967 \qquad 779 + 766 \qquad 492 + 768 \qquad 657 + 756 \qquad 999 + 456 \qquad 695 + 908$$

6.
$$935 + 896 \qquad 888 + 764 \qquad 339 + 664 \qquad 757 + 994 \qquad 864 + 686 \qquad 681 + 459$$

7.
$$975 + 358 \qquad 756 + 489 \qquad 505 + 796 \qquad 787 + 835 \qquad 759 + 746 \qquad 649 + 962$$

Addition Word Problems

Name_____ Date_____

Fill in the circle next to the correct sum.

1. For the charity raffle, the video store donated $142 worth of VHS tapes and $236 worth of DVDs. What was the total value of the store's donation?

   ○ a) $278   ○ b) $328   ○ c) $378   ○ d) $358

2. The toy store donated $482 worth of toys and another $249 worth of gift certificates. What was the total value of the toy store's donation?

   ○ a) $731   ○ b) $732   ○ c) $721   ○ d) $631

3. The electronics store donated a TV worth $569 and a camcorder worth $249. What was the total value of the electronics store's donation?

   ○ a) $818   ○ b) $908   ○ c) $808   ○ d) $918

4. What was the combined value of donations from the video store and the toy store?

   ○ a) $909   ○ b) $1,109   ○ c) $1,019   ○ d) $919

5. On the first day of raffle tickets sales, $573 was raised. The next day, $392 was raised. How much money was raised the first two days?

   ○ a) $955   ○ b) $945   ○ c) $975   ○ d) $965

6. Another $376 was raised on the third day, and $588 was raised on the fourth day. How much money in ticket sales was raised on the third and fourth days?

   ○ a) $962   ○ b) $964   ○ c) $968   ○ d) $974

7. The charity accountant added the total dollars raised during the first two days of ticket sales with the amount raised the next two days. What was that total?

   ○ a) $2,029   ○ b) $1,929   ○ c) $1,829   ○ d) $1,839

Name_____ Date_____

586	First subtract	586	Then subtract	586	Finally, subtract
−213	the ones.	−213	the tens.	−213	the hundreds.
3		**7**3		**37**3	

Subtract.

1.
```
  300      800      740      690      530      485
 -100     -500     -320     -570     -120     -325
```

2.
```
  548      837      995      696      388      596
 -226     -325     -473     -293     -124     -461
```

3.
```
  894      327      564      392      967      428
 -632     -116     -123     -170     -532     -201
```

4.
```
  385      488      913      579      766      375
 -224     -167     -802     -455     -431     -234
```

5.
```
  284      738      894      585      946      757
 -133     -602     -551     -323     -435     -523
```

6.
```
  958      647      952      555      481      879
 -745     -522     -640     -314     -261     -734
```

7.
```
  966      449      386      825      598      649
 -243     -217     -142     -305     -126     -438
```

Subtraction: Regrouping

Name_____ Date_____

$$\begin{array}{r}{\scriptstyle 1\ 10}\\ 4\,\not2\,\not0\\ -\ 16\,4\\ \hline 6\end{array}$$ First regroup the tens and ones. Subtract the ones.

$$\begin{array}{r}{\scriptstyle 3\ 11\ 10}\\ \not4\,\not2\,\not0\\ -\ 16\,4\\ \hline 5\,6\end{array}$$ Then regroup the hundreds and tens. Subtract the tens.

$$\begin{array}{r}{\scriptstyle 3\ 11\ 10}\\ 4\,2\,0\\ -\ 16\,4\\ \hline 2\,5\,6\end{array}$$ Finally, subtract the hundreds.

Unit 3

Subtract.

1. 432 − 126	385 − 197	234 − 117	612 − 386	844 − 578	752 − 364
2. 357 − 219	705 − 618	287 − 178	656 − 289	833 − 745	928 − 549
3. 461 − 283	232 − 156	724 − 437	811 − 452	502 − 319	732 − 554
4. 670 − 489	700 − 327	473 − 198	236 − 157	814 − 349	523 − 264
5. 615 − 389	367 − 178	621 − 291	540 − 167	800 − 593	404 − 275
6. 300 − 156	791 − 395	264 − 168	824 − 527	515 − 266	606 − 159
7. 573 − 284	841 − 457	235 − 118	307 − 184	736 − 258	504 − 369

Subtraction Word Problems

Name_____ Date_____

Fill in the circle next to the correct difference.

1. There are 147 people watching a movie in Theatre A. The theatre has a total of 280 seats. How many seats are empty?
   ○ a) 143   ○ b) 133   ○ c) 132   ○ d) 134

2. Theatre B has 422 seats, and there are 184 people watching the 2:00 p.m. showing there. How many seats are empty?
   ○ a) 236   ○ b) 248   ○ c) 242   ○ d) 238

3. Theatre C has only 213 seats, but 508 people want to see the 7:00 p.m. showing there. How many people cannot see that showing?
   ○ a) 295   ○ b) 296   ○ c) 285   ○ d) 286

4. The concessions stand manager ordered 700 boxes of chocolate-covered raisins. A total of 263 boxes were sold in one day. How many are left?
   ○ a) 337   ○ b) 449   ○ c) 347   ○ d) 437

5. The manager also ordered 850 large popcorn bags. On Saturday, 419 bags were used. How many bags are left?
   ○ a) 331   ○ b) 441   ○ c) 341   ○ d) 431

6. On Sunday, the concessions stand sold 923 colas and 484 fruit drinks. How many more colas than fruit drinks were sold?
   ○ a) 539   ○ b) 439   ○ c) 449   ○ d) 438

7. On average, 597 children and 914 adults visit the movie multiplex each Sunday. How many more adults visit than children?
   ○ a) 317   ○ b) 397   ○ c) 417   ○ d) 307

Name_____ Date_____

Use the chart to answer the problems. Write and solve an equation for each problem. Circle **A** if you added to solve it. Circle **S** if you subtracted.

LIBRARY BOOKS CHECKED OUT			
Subject	April	May	June
Pets	452	679	730
Sports	635	820	951
Music	387	223	354

Unit 3

1. How many more pet books were checked out in June than in May?

+/– ☐ **A**
☐ ☐ **S**
☐

2. Altogether, how many sports books were checked out in April and May?

+/– ☐ **A**
☐ ☐ **S**
☐

3. How many more pet books than music books were checked out in June?

+/– ☐ **A**
☐ ☐ **S**
☐

4. How many fewer music books than sports books were checked out in April?

+/– ☐ **A**
☐ ☐ **S**
☐

5. Altogether, how many pet books were checked out in April and May?

+/– ☐ **A**
☐ ☐ **S**
☐

6. How many more sports books than music books were checked out in June?

+/– ☐ **A**
☐ ☐ **S**
☐

Name_____ Date_____

1. Count by 6s to complete the chart.

x	0	1	2	3	4	5	6	7	8	9
6	0	6	12							

Multiply.

2.
$$\begin{array}{r} 0 \\ \times\,6 \\ \hline \end{array} \quad \begin{array}{r} 7 \\ \times\,6 \\ \hline \end{array} \quad \begin{array}{r} 6 \\ \times\,6 \\ \hline \end{array} \quad \begin{array}{r} 6 \\ \times\,3 \\ \hline \end{array} \quad \begin{array}{r} 5 \\ \times\,6 \\ \hline \end{array} \quad \begin{array}{r} 6 \\ \times\,9 \\ \hline \end{array}$$

3.
$$\begin{array}{r} 2 \\ \times\,6 \\ \hline \end{array} \quad \begin{array}{r} 3 \\ \times\,4 \\ \hline \end{array} \quad \begin{array}{r} 4 \\ \times\,9 \\ \hline \end{array} \quad \begin{array}{r} 3 \\ \times\,6 \\ \hline \end{array} \quad \begin{array}{r} 6 \\ \times\,1 \\ \hline \end{array} \quad \begin{array}{r} 8 \\ \times\,6 \\ \hline \end{array}$$

4.
$$\begin{array}{r} 6 \\ \times\,7 \\ \hline \end{array} \quad \begin{array}{r} 5 \\ \times\,7 \\ \hline \end{array} \quad \begin{array}{r} 4 \\ \times\,3 \\ \hline \end{array} \quad \begin{array}{r} 6 \\ \times\,8 \\ \hline \end{array} \quad \begin{array}{r} 6 \\ \times\,2 \\ \hline \end{array} \quad \begin{array}{r} 4 \\ \times\,6 \\ \hline \end{array}$$

5.
$$\begin{array}{r} 9 \\ \times\,6 \\ \hline \end{array} \quad \begin{array}{r} 1 \\ \times\,6 \\ \hline \end{array} \quad \begin{array}{r} 6 \\ \times\,4 \\ \hline \end{array} \quad \begin{array}{r} 6 \\ \times\,0 \\ \hline \end{array} \quad \begin{array}{r} 5 \\ \times\,5 \\ \hline \end{array} \quad \begin{array}{r} 6 \\ \times\,5 \\ \hline \end{array}$$

Write and solve a multiplication equation for each problem.

6. The gym teacher divided his class into six groups
   of five. How many students are in the class?   ____ x ____ = ____

7. Each group was given three basketballs to share.
   How many basketballs were given out?   ____ x ____ = ____

Name_____ Date_____

1. Count by 7s to complete the chart.

x	0	1	2	3	4	5	6	7	8	9
7	0	7	14							

Multiply.

2.
7 × 7
7 × 3
6 × 7
7 × 8
7 × 1
4 × 7

3.
0 × 7
4 × 5
7 × 9
3 × 7
7 × 2
8 × 7

4.
7 × 4
1 × 7
4 × 9
7 × 0
6 × 3
7 × 5

5.
9 × 7
2 × 7
7 × 6
3 × 9
5 × 7
8 × 4

Write and solve a multiplication equation for each problem.

6. Jasmine swam six laps each day for one whole week.
How many laps did she swim by the end of the week? ____ x ____ = ____

7. Kyle performed seven high dives a day for nine days.
How many high dives did he perform in all? ____ x ____ = ____

Name_____ Date_____

1. Count by 8s to complete the chart.

x	0	1	2	3	4	5	6	7	8	9
8	0	8	16							

Multiply.

2.
$\begin{array}{r} 8 \\ \times\,4 \\ \hline \end{array}$
$\begin{array}{r} 1 \\ \times\,8 \\ \hline \end{array}$
$\begin{array}{r} 5 \\ \times\,8 \\ \hline \end{array}$
$\begin{array}{r} 8 \\ \times\,0 \\ \hline \end{array}$
$\begin{array}{r} 4 \\ \times\,6 \\ \hline \end{array}$
$\begin{array}{r} 8 \\ \times\,5 \\ \hline \end{array}$

3.
$\begin{array}{r} 9 \\ \times\,8 \\ \hline \end{array}$
$\begin{array}{r} 2 \\ \times\,8 \\ \hline \end{array}$
$\begin{array}{r} 8 \\ \times\,6 \\ \hline \end{array}$
$\begin{array}{r} 3 \\ \times\,9 \\ \hline \end{array}$
$\begin{array}{r} 8 \\ \times\,7 \\ \hline \end{array}$
$\begin{array}{r} 7 \\ \times\,6 \\ \hline \end{array}$

4.
$\begin{array}{r} 8 \\ \times\,8 \\ \hline \end{array}$
$\begin{array}{r} 8 \\ \times\,3 \\ \hline \end{array}$
$\begin{array}{r} 6 \\ \times\,8 \\ \hline \end{array}$
$\begin{array}{r} 6 \\ \times\,3 \\ \hline \end{array}$
$\begin{array}{r} 8 \\ \times\,1 \\ \hline \end{array}$
$\begin{array}{r} 4 \\ \times\,8 \\ \hline \end{array}$

5.
$\begin{array}{r} 0 \\ \times\,8 \\ \hline \end{array}$
$\begin{array}{r} 7 \\ \times\,9 \\ \hline \end{array}$
$\begin{array}{r} 8 \\ \times\,9 \\ \hline \end{array}$
$\begin{array}{r} 3 \\ \times\,8 \\ \hline \end{array}$
$\begin{array}{r} 8 \\ \times\,2 \\ \hline \end{array}$
$\begin{array}{r} 7 \\ \times\,8 \\ \hline \end{array}$

Write and solve a multiplication equation for each problem.

6. Mrs. Carter bought seven boxes of crayons. Each box has eight crayons. How many crayons are there in all? _____ x _____ = _____

7. Mrs. Leroy bought eight packs of erasers. Each pack holds four erasers. How many erasers are there in all? _____ x _____ = _____

Multiplication Facts (IV)

Name_____ Date_____

1. Count by 9s to complete the chart.

x	0	1	2	3	4	5	6	7	8	9
9	0	9	18							

Multiply.

2.
$$\begin{array}{r} 9 \\ \times\, 4 \\ \hline \end{array}$$
$$\begin{array}{r} 1 \\ \times\, 9 \\ \hline \end{array}$$
$$\begin{array}{r} 9 \\ \times\, 9 \\ \hline \end{array}$$
$$\begin{array}{r} 9 \\ \times\, 0 \\ \hline \end{array}$$
$$\begin{array}{r} 7 \\ \times\, 7 \\ \hline \end{array}$$
$$\begin{array}{r} 9 \\ \times\, 5 \\ \hline \end{array}$$

3.
$$\begin{array}{r} 2 \\ \times\, 9 \\ \hline \end{array}$$
$$\begin{array}{r} 8 \\ \times\, 7 \\ \hline \end{array}$$
$$\begin{array}{r} 6 \\ \times\, 6 \\ \hline \end{array}$$
$$\begin{array}{r} 3 \\ \times\, 9 \\ \hline \end{array}$$
$$\begin{array}{r} 9 \\ \times\, 2 \\ \hline \end{array}$$
$$\begin{array}{r} 8 \\ \times\, 9 \\ \hline \end{array}$$

4.
$$\begin{array}{r} 9 \\ \times\, 7 \\ \hline \end{array}$$
$$\begin{array}{r} 9 \\ \times\, 3 \\ \hline \end{array}$$
$$\begin{array}{r} 6 \\ \times\, 9 \\ \hline \end{array}$$
$$\begin{array}{r} 9 \\ \times\, 8 \\ \hline \end{array}$$
$$\begin{array}{r} 9 \\ \times\, 1 \\ \hline \end{array}$$
$$\begin{array}{r} 4 \\ \times\, 9 \\ \hline \end{array}$$

5.
$$\begin{array}{r} 0 \\ \times\, 9 \\ \hline \end{array}$$
$$\begin{array}{r} 7 \\ \times\, 9 \\ \hline \end{array}$$
$$\begin{array}{r} 9 \\ \times\, 6 \\ \hline \end{array}$$
$$\begin{array}{r} 8 \\ \times\, 3 \\ \hline \end{array}$$
$$\begin{array}{r} 5 \\ \times\, 9 \\ \hline \end{array}$$
$$\begin{array}{r} 6 \\ \times\, 8 \\ \hline \end{array}$$

Write and solve a multiplication equation for each problem.

6. An apartment house has five floors. Each floor has nine apartments. How many apartments are there in all?

_____ x _____ = _____

7. A hotel has nine floors. Each floor has eight rooms. How many rooms are there in all?

_____ x _____ = _____

Name_____ Date_____

1. Complete the multiplication chart.

x	0	1	2	3	4	5	6	7	8	9
6			12					42		
7	0									
8		8				40				
9	0		18							

Find the missing factor.

2.   7 x ____ = 49   8 x ____ = 72   ____ x 5 = 45   8 x ____ = 32

3.   ____ x 9 = 36   ____ x 3 = 24   6 x ____ = 54   ____ x 6 = 36

4.   2 x ____ = 14   ____ x 6 = 42   7 x ____ = 63   ____ x 5 = 40

5.   ____ x 5 = 30   4 x ____ = 28   ____ x 9 = 81   7 x ____ = 21

6.   5 x ____ = 35   8 x ____ = 56   ____ x 8 = 48   6 x ____ = 42

7.   ____ x 2 = 16   3 x ____ = 27   ____ x 8 = 64   9 x ____ = 54

Multiplication Facts Drill (I)

Name_____ Date_____

Multiply.

1.
$$\begin{array}{r} 1 \\ \times\,8 \\ \hline \end{array}$$
$$\begin{array}{r} 2 \\ \times\,7 \\ \hline \end{array}$$
$$\begin{array}{r} 7 \\ \times\,6 \\ \hline \end{array}$$
$$\begin{array}{r} 8 \\ \times\,3 \\ \hline \end{array}$$
$$\begin{array}{r} 9 \\ \times\,2 \\ \hline \end{array}$$
$$\begin{array}{r} 6 \\ \times\,1 \\ \hline \end{array}$$

2.
$$\begin{array}{r} 7 \\ \times\,7 \\ \hline \end{array}$$
$$\begin{array}{r} 6 \\ \times\,8 \\ \hline \end{array}$$
$$\begin{array}{r} 9 \\ \times\,9 \\ \hline \end{array}$$
$$\begin{array}{r} 3 \\ \times\,7 \\ \hline \end{array}$$
$$\begin{array}{r} 7 \\ \times\,2 \\ \hline \end{array}$$
$$\begin{array}{r} 6 \\ \times\,4 \\ \hline \end{array}$$

3.
$$\begin{array}{r} 2 \\ \times\,8 \\ \hline \end{array}$$
$$\begin{array}{r} 9 \\ \times\,1 \\ \hline \end{array}$$
$$\begin{array}{r} 3 \\ \times\,6 \\ \hline \end{array}$$
$$\begin{array}{r} 7 \\ \times\,9 \\ \hline \end{array}$$
$$\begin{array}{r} 4 \\ \times\,8 \\ \hline \end{array}$$
$$\begin{array}{r} 8 \\ \times\,9 \\ \hline \end{array}$$

4.
$$\begin{array}{r} 6 \\ \times\,7 \\ \hline \end{array}$$
$$\begin{array}{r} 5 \\ \times\,9 \\ \hline \end{array}$$
$$\begin{array}{r} 9 \\ \times\,4 \\ \hline \end{array}$$
$$\begin{array}{r} 5 \\ \times\,6 \\ \hline \end{array}$$
$$\begin{array}{r} 0 \\ \times\,6 \\ \hline \end{array}$$
$$\begin{array}{r} 8 \\ \times\,5 \\ \hline \end{array}$$

5.
$$\begin{array}{r} 0 \\ \times\,7 \\ \hline \end{array}$$
$$\begin{array}{r} 6 \\ \times\,5 \\ \hline \end{array}$$
$$\begin{array}{r} 2 \\ \times\,6 \\ \hline \end{array}$$
$$\begin{array}{r} 8 \\ \times\,4 \\ \hline \end{array}$$
$$\begin{array}{r} 9 \\ \times\,6 \\ \hline \end{array}$$
$$\begin{array}{r} 7 \\ \times\,8 \\ \hline \end{array}$$

6.
$$\begin{array}{r} 6 \\ \times\,3 \\ \hline \end{array}$$
$$\begin{array}{r} 1 \\ \times\,9 \\ \hline \end{array}$$
$$\begin{array}{r} 7 \\ \times\,5 \\ \hline \end{array}$$
$$\begin{array}{r} 8 \\ \times\,2 \\ \hline \end{array}$$
$$\begin{array}{r} 9 \\ \times\,3 \\ \hline \end{array}$$
$$\begin{array}{r} 3 \\ \times\,8 \\ \hline \end{array}$$

7.
$$\begin{array}{r} 9 \\ \times\,5 \\ \hline \end{array}$$
$$\begin{array}{r} 0 \\ \times\,9 \\ \hline \end{array}$$
$$\begin{array}{r} 3 \\ \times\,9 \\ \hline \end{array}$$
$$\begin{array}{r} 6 \\ \times\,9 \\ \hline \end{array}$$
$$\begin{array}{r} 7 \\ \times\,4 \\ \hline \end{array}$$
$$\begin{array}{r} 8 \\ \times\,6 \\ \hline \end{array}$$

8.
$$\begin{array}{r} 9 \\ \times\,8 \\ \hline \end{array}$$
$$\begin{array}{r} 6 \\ \times\,2 \\ \hline \end{array}$$
$$\begin{array}{r} 7 \\ \times\,3 \\ \hline \end{array}$$
$$\begin{array}{r} 8 \\ \times\,7 \\ \hline \end{array}$$
$$\begin{array}{r} 8 \\ \times\,8 \\ \hline \end{array}$$
$$\begin{array}{r} 1 \\ \times\,7 \\ \hline \end{array}$$

9.
$$\begin{array}{r} 9 \\ \times\,7 \\ \hline \end{array}$$
$$\begin{array}{r} 4 \\ \times\,6 \\ \hline \end{array}$$
$$\begin{array}{r} 1 \\ \times\,6 \\ \hline \end{array}$$
$$\begin{array}{r} 4 \\ \times\,9 \\ \hline \end{array}$$
$$\begin{array}{r} 5 \\ \times\,7 \\ \hline \end{array}$$
$$\begin{array}{r} 2 \\ \times\,9 \\ \hline \end{array}$$

10.
$$\begin{array}{r} 8 \\ \times\,1 \\ \hline \end{array}$$
$$\begin{array}{r} 5 \\ \times\,8 \\ \hline \end{array}$$
$$\begin{array}{r} 0 \\ \times\,8 \\ \hline \end{array}$$
$$\begin{array}{r} 7 \\ \times\,1 \\ \hline \end{array}$$
$$\begin{array}{r} 4 \\ \times\,7 \\ \hline \end{array}$$
$$\begin{array}{r} 6 \\ \times\,6 \\ \hline \end{array}$$

Name_____ Date_____

Multiply.

1.
$\begin{array}{r} 1 \\ \times 8 \\ \hline \end{array}$
$\begin{array}{r} 4 \\ \times 3 \\ \hline \end{array}$
$\begin{array}{r} 3 \\ \times 5 \\ \hline \end{array}$
$\begin{array}{r} 6 \\ \times 4 \\ \hline \end{array}$
$\begin{array}{r} 2 \\ \times 7 \\ \hline \end{array}$
$\begin{array}{r} 9 \\ \times 4 \\ \hline \end{array}$

2.
$\begin{array}{r} 5 \\ \times 3 \\ \hline \end{array}$
$\begin{array}{r} 5 \\ \times 8 \\ \hline \end{array}$
$\begin{array}{r} 7 \\ \times 9 \\ \hline \end{array}$
$\begin{array}{r} 8 \\ \times 6 \\ \hline \end{array}$
$\begin{array}{r} 0 \\ \times 2 \\ \hline \end{array}$
$\begin{array}{r} 8 \\ \times 4 \\ \hline \end{array}$

3.
$\begin{array}{r} 3 \\ \times 8 \\ \hline \end{array}$
$\begin{array}{r} 7 \\ \times 6 \\ \hline \end{array}$
$\begin{array}{r} 4 \\ \times 5 \\ \hline \end{array}$
$\begin{array}{r} 3 \\ \times 4 \\ \hline \end{array}$
$\begin{array}{r} 6 \\ \times 8 \\ \hline \end{array}$
$\begin{array}{r} 4 \\ \times 9 \\ \hline \end{array}$

4.
$\begin{array}{r} 6 \\ \times 3 \\ \hline \end{array}$
$\begin{array}{r} 2 \\ \times 9 \\ \hline \end{array}$
$\begin{array}{r} 8 \\ \times 3 \\ \hline \end{array}$
$\begin{array}{r} 5 \\ \times 2 \\ \hline \end{array}$
$\begin{array}{r} 1 \\ \times 5 \\ \hline \end{array}$
$\begin{array}{r} 5 \\ \times 6 \\ \hline \end{array}$

5.
$\begin{array}{r} 9 \\ \times 1 \\ \hline \end{array}$
$\begin{array}{r} 3 \\ \times 7 \\ \hline \end{array}$
$\begin{array}{r} 9 \\ \times 6 \\ \hline \end{array}$
$\begin{array}{r} 2 \\ \times 4 \\ \hline \end{array}$
$\begin{array}{r} 0 \\ \times 5 \\ \hline \end{array}$
$\begin{array}{r} 4 \\ \times 8 \\ \hline \end{array}$

6.
$\begin{array}{r} 7 \\ \times 3 \\ \hline \end{array}$
$\begin{array}{r} 0 \\ \times 9 \\ \hline \end{array}$
$\begin{array}{r} 6 \\ \times 5 \\ \hline \end{array}$
$\begin{array}{r} 1 \\ \times 7 \\ \hline \end{array}$
$\begin{array}{r} 9 \\ \times 3 \\ \hline \end{array}$
$\begin{array}{r} 8 \\ \times 5 \\ \hline \end{array}$

7.
$\begin{array}{r} 3 \\ \times 6 \\ \hline \end{array}$
$\begin{array}{r} 1 \\ \times 6 \\ \hline \end{array}$
$\begin{array}{r} 4 \\ \times 7 \\ \hline \end{array}$
$\begin{array}{r} 3 \\ \times 9 \\ \hline \end{array}$
$\begin{array}{r} 7 \\ \times 4 \\ \hline \end{array}$
$\begin{array}{r} 5 \\ \times 0 \\ \hline \end{array}$

8.
$\begin{array}{r} 0 \\ \times 8 \\ \hline \end{array}$
$\begin{array}{r} 2 \\ \times 8 \\ \hline \end{array}$
$\begin{array}{r} 4 \\ \times 1 \\ \hline \end{array}$
$\begin{array}{r} 5 \\ \times 4 \\ \hline \end{array}$
$\begin{array}{r} 9 \\ \times 8 \\ \hline \end{array}$
$\begin{array}{r} 6 \\ \times 2 \\ \hline \end{array}$

9.
$\begin{array}{r} 2 \\ \times 0 \\ \hline \end{array}$
$\begin{array}{r} 7 \\ \times 5 \\ \hline \end{array}$
$\begin{array}{r} 9 \\ \times 5 \\ \hline \end{array}$
$\begin{array}{r} 8 \\ \times 7 \\ \hline \end{array}$
$\begin{array}{r} 0 \\ \times 1 \\ \hline \end{array}$
$\begin{array}{r} 1 \\ \times 9 \\ \hline \end{array}$

10.
$\begin{array}{r} 2 \\ \times 1 \\ \hline \end{array}$
$\begin{array}{r} 4 \\ \times 4 \\ \hline \end{array}$
$\begin{array}{r} 5 \\ \times 6 \\ \hline \end{array}$
$\begin{array}{r} 3 \\ \times 1 \\ \hline \end{array}$
$\begin{array}{r} 6 \\ \times 8 \\ \hline \end{array}$
$\begin{array}{r} 8 \\ \times 6 \\ \hline \end{array}$

Multiplication Facts Review

Name_____ Date_____

Fill in the circle next to the correct product.

1. **6 x 7 =**
   - ○ a) 41
   - ○ b) 48
   - ○ c) 42
   - ○ d) 36

   8 x 6 =
   - ○ a) 42
   - ○ b) 64
   - ○ c) 48
   - ○ d) 56

   7 x 3 =
   - ○ a) 14
   - ○ b) 18
   - ○ c) 21
   - ○ d) 24

2. **9 x 9 =**
   - ○ a) 72
   - ○ b) 64
   - ○ c) 99
   - ○ d) 81

   4 x 7 =
   - ○ a) 27
   - ○ b) 28
   - ○ c) 24
   - ○ d) 21

   9 x 5 =
   - ○ a) 40
   - ○ b) 35
   - ○ c) 45
   - ○ d) 50

3. **4 x 6 =**
   - ○ a) 24
   - ○ b) 18
   - ○ c) 32
   - ○ d) 36

   8 x 9 =
   - ○ a) 64
   - ○ b) 72
   - ○ c) 56
   - ○ d) 54

   7 x 8 =
   - ○ a) 56
   - ○ b) 48
   - ○ c) 54
   - ○ d) 63

4. **5 x 8 =**
   - ○ a) 35
   - ○ b) 40
   - ○ c) 48
   - ○ d) 30

   6 x 6 =
   - ○ a) 42
   - ○ b) 48
   - ○ c) 36
   - ○ d) 30

   7 x 7 =
   - ○ a) 39
   - ○ b) 42
   - ○ c) 49
   - ○ d) 48

5. **9 x 7 =**
   - ○ a) 56
   - ○ b) 63
   - ○ c) 64
   - ○ d) 72

   8 x 8 =
   - ○ a) 68
   - ○ b) 56
   - ○ c) 64
   - ○ d) 72

   7 x 2 =
   - ○ a) 14
   - ○ b) 18
   - ○ c) 12
   - ○ d) 16

6. **4 x 8 =**
   - ○ a) 24
   - ○ b) 32
   - ○ c) 28
   - ○ d) 36

   5 x 5 =
   - ○ a) 20
   - ○ b) 15
   - ○ c) 30
   - ○ d) 25

   5 x 6 =
   - ○ a) 30
   - ○ b) 25
   - ○ c) 35
   - ○ d) 40

7. **8 x 2 =**
   - ○ a) 12
   - ○ b) 16
   - ○ c) 14
   - ○ d) 18

   7 x 5 =
   - ○ a) 45
   - ○ b) 30
   - ○ c) 35
   - ○ d) 40

   3 x 9 =
   - ○ a) 27
   - ○ b) 21
   - ○ c) 28
   - ○ d) 36

Multiplication Word Problems (1)

Name_____ Date_____

Read each problem then write an equation to solve it.

1. At the fair, six people can run the egg-and-spoon race at one time. There are eight races. How many total people can run the egg-and spoon race?

   x [ ]
   ___
   [ ]

2. Six people can run the three-legged race at one time. There are nine races. How many total people can run the three-legged race?

   x [ ]
   ___
   [ ]

3. Each Ferris wheel carriage holds five people. There are nine carriages. How many people can ride at one time?

   x [ ]
   ___
   [ ]

4. The roller coaster has eight cars. Three people fit into each car. How many people can ride at one time?

   x [ ]
   ___
   [ ]

5. Saltwater taffy is sold seven pieces for one dollar. How many pieces can eight dollars buy?

   x [ ]
   ___
   [ ]

6. Game booth tickets are sold six for one dollar. How many tickets can five dollars buy?

   x [ ]
   ___
   [ ]

7. Extra-large balloons cost three dollars apiece. How many dollars do nine balloons cost?

   x [ ]
   ___
   [ ]

Multiplication (I)

Name_____ Date_____

```
 12
x 4    First multiply 2 ones by 4 ones.
 8
```

```
 12
x 4    Then multiply 1 ten by 4 ones.
48
```

Unit 3

Multiply.

1.	10	11	10	11	10	12

1.
```
  10      11      10      11      10      12
 x 3     x 3     x 6     x 2     x 1     x 3
```

2.
```
  11      10      12      11      11      10
 x 7     x 9     x 0     x 1     x 4     x 5
```

3.
```
  11      10      12      11      10      20
 x 8     x 7     x 1     x 9     x 4     x 1
```

4.
```
  10      11      12      11      12      10
 x 8     x 5     x 4     x 6     x 2     x 2
```

5.
```
  20      30      20      40      30      20
 x 2     x 2     x 4     x 2     x 3     x 3
```

Read each problem then write an equation to solve it.

6. The baker used three dozen eggs to make
   cookies. How many eggs did she use in all?

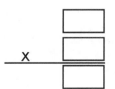

7. She sold the cookies for ten cents apiece.
   How many cents did nine cookies cost?

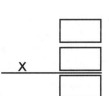

Premium Education Math: Grade 3   69   © Learning Horizons

Name_____ Date_____

Multiply.

1.
  20   44   13   23   27   30
  x 2   x 2   x 3   x 2   x 1   x 2

2.
  21   32   43   31   24   22
  x 4   x 3   x 2   x 2   x 2   x 4

3.
  30   23   14   13   41   20
  x 3   x 3   x 2   x 2   x 2   x 3

4.
  22   31   21   29   34   22
  x 3   x 3   x 3   x 1   x 2   x 2

5.
  21   12   23   25   42   32
  x 2   x 3   x 3   x 1   x 2   x 2

Read each problem then write an equation to solve it.

6. Jim ate two bananas each day for three weeks.
How many bananas did he eat in all?

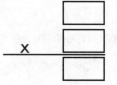

7. Beth ate two apples each day for two weeks.
How many apples did she eat in all?

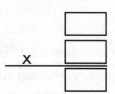

Multiplication: Regrouping (I)

Name_____ Date_____

$\overset{2}{1}4$ First, multiply 4 ones by 6 ones.
$\underline{\times\ 6}$ Regroup the extra tens.
4

$\overset{2}{1}4$ Then multiply 1 ten by 6 ones.
$\underline{\times\ 6}$ Add the 2 extra tens.
84

Multiply.

1.
$\begin{array}{r}12\\ \times\ 5\\ \hline\end{array}$
$\begin{array}{r}14\\ \times\ 3\\ \hline\end{array}$
$\begin{array}{r}15\\ \times\ 3\\ \hline\end{array}$
$\begin{array}{r}23\\ \times\ 4\\ \hline\end{array}$
$\begin{array}{r}16\\ \times\ 5\\ \hline\end{array}$
$\begin{array}{r}12\\ \times\ 7\\ \hline\end{array}$

2.
$\begin{array}{r}13\\ \times\ 7\\ \hline\end{array}$
$\begin{array}{r}17\\ \times\ 5\\ \hline\end{array}$
$\begin{array}{r}12\\ \times\ 8\\ \hline\end{array}$
$\begin{array}{r}19\\ \times\ 2\\ \hline\end{array}$
$\begin{array}{r}36\\ \times\ 2\\ \hline\end{array}$
$\begin{array}{r}18\\ \times\ 5\\ \hline\end{array}$

3.
$\begin{array}{r}12\\ \times\ 6\\ \hline\end{array}$
$\begin{array}{r}24\\ \times\ 3\\ \hline\end{array}$
$\begin{array}{r}16\\ \times\ 3\\ \hline\end{array}$
$\begin{array}{r}28\\ \times\ 3\\ \hline\end{array}$
$\begin{array}{r}15\\ \times\ 6\\ \hline\end{array}$
$\begin{array}{r}14\\ \times\ 4\\ \hline\end{array}$

4.
$\begin{array}{r}27\\ \times\ 2\\ \hline\end{array}$
$\begin{array}{r}38\\ \times\ 2\\ \hline\end{array}$
$\begin{array}{r}19\\ \times\ 4\\ \hline\end{array}$
$\begin{array}{r}24\\ \times\ 4\\ \hline\end{array}$
$\begin{array}{r}17\\ \times\ 2\\ \hline\end{array}$
$\begin{array}{r}25\\ \times\ 2\\ \hline\end{array}$

5.
$\begin{array}{r}16\\ \times\ 4\\ \hline\end{array}$
$\begin{array}{r}29\\ \times\ 3\\ \hline\end{array}$
$\begin{array}{r}13\\ \times\ 5\\ \hline\end{array}$
$\begin{array}{r}39\\ \times\ 2\\ \hline\end{array}$
$\begin{array}{r}37\\ \times\ 2\\ \hline\end{array}$
$\begin{array}{r}18\\ \times\ 3\\ \hline\end{array}$

6.
$\begin{array}{r}17\\ \times\ 3\\ \hline\end{array}$
$\begin{array}{r}16\\ \times\ 2\\ \hline\end{array}$
$\begin{array}{r}28\\ \times\ 2\\ \hline\end{array}$
$\begin{array}{r}35\\ \times\ 2\\ \hline\end{array}$
$\begin{array}{r}17\\ \times\ 4\\ \hline\end{array}$
$\begin{array}{r}14\\ \times\ 5\\ \hline\end{array}$

7.
$\begin{array}{r}18\\ \times\ 2\\ \hline\end{array}$
$\begin{array}{r}25\\ \times\ 3\\ \hline\end{array}$
$\begin{array}{r}15\\ \times\ 5\\ \hline\end{array}$
$\begin{array}{r}16\\ \times\ 6\\ \hline\end{array}$
$\begin{array}{r}18\\ \times\ 4\\ \hline\end{array}$
$\begin{array}{r}19\\ \times\ 3\\ \hline\end{array}$

Multiplication: Regrouping (II)

Name_____ Date_____

$$\begin{array}{r} 70 \\ \times\ 6 \\ \hline 0 \end{array}$$ First, multiply 0 by 6 ones.

$$\begin{array}{r} ^4\,70 \\ \times\ 6 \\ \hline 20 \end{array}$$ Then multiply 7 tens by 6 ones. Regroup the extra hundreds.

$$\begin{array}{r} ^4\,70 \\ \times\ 6 \\ \hline 420 \end{array}$$ Finally, add the hundreds.

THINK: 7 ones x 6 ones = 42 ones → 7 tens x 6 ones = 42 tens or 420

Multiply.

1.
$$\begin{array}{r} 40 \\ \times\ 5 \\ \hline \end{array}$$
$$\begin{array}{r} 60 \\ \times\ 7 \\ \hline \end{array}$$
$$\begin{array}{r} 80 \\ \times\ 3 \\ \hline \end{array}$$
$$\begin{array}{r} 50 \\ \times\ 6 \\ \hline \end{array}$$
$$\begin{array}{r} 30 \\ \times\ 5 \\ \hline \end{array}$$
$$\begin{array}{r} 20 \\ \times\ 7 \\ \hline \end{array}$$

2.
$$\begin{array}{r} 90 \\ \times\ 7 \\ \hline \end{array}$$
$$\begin{array}{r} 70 \\ \times\ 4 \\ \hline \end{array}$$
$$\begin{array}{r} 40 \\ \times\ 8 \\ \hline \end{array}$$
$$\begin{array}{r} 60 \\ \times\ 9 \\ \hline \end{array}$$
$$\begin{array}{r} 80 \\ \times\ 6 \\ \hline \end{array}$$
$$\begin{array}{r} 50 \\ \times\ 9 \\ \hline \end{array}$$

3.
$$\begin{array}{r} 30 \\ \times\ 8 \\ \hline \end{array}$$
$$\begin{array}{r} 20 \\ \times\ 9 \\ \hline \end{array}$$
$$\begin{array}{r} 90 \\ \times\ 8 \\ \hline \end{array}$$
$$\begin{array}{r} 70 \\ \times\ 5 \\ \hline \end{array}$$
$$\begin{array}{r} 40 \\ \times\ 6 \\ \hline \end{array}$$
$$\begin{array}{r} 60 \\ \times\ 5 \\ \hline \end{array}$$

4.
$$\begin{array}{r} 80 \\ \times\ 4 \\ \hline \end{array}$$
$$\begin{array}{r} 50 \\ \times\ 7 \\ \hline \end{array}$$
$$\begin{array}{r} 30 \\ \times\ 7 \\ \hline \end{array}$$
$$\begin{array}{r} 20 \\ \times\ 5 \\ \hline \end{array}$$
$$\begin{array}{r} 90 \\ \times\ 4 \\ \hline \end{array}$$
$$\begin{array}{r} 70 \\ \times\ 8 \\ \hline \end{array}$$

5.
$$\begin{array}{r} 40 \\ \times\ 4 \\ \hline \end{array}$$
$$\begin{array}{r} 60 \\ \times\ 8 \\ \hline \end{array}$$
$$\begin{array}{r} 80 \\ \times\ 7 \\ \hline \end{array}$$
$$\begin{array}{r} 50 \\ \times\ 5 \\ \hline \end{array}$$
$$\begin{array}{r} 30 \\ \times\ 9 \\ \hline \end{array}$$
$$\begin{array}{r} 20 \\ \times\ 8 \\ \hline \end{array}$$

6.
$$\begin{array}{r} 90 \\ \times\ 9 \\ \hline \end{array}$$
$$\begin{array}{r} 70 \\ \times\ 7 \\ \hline \end{array}$$
$$\begin{array}{r} 40 \\ \times\ 9 \\ \hline \end{array}$$
$$\begin{array}{r} 60 \\ \times\ 6 \\ \hline \end{array}$$
$$\begin{array}{r} 80 \\ \times\ 8 \\ \hline \end{array}$$
$$\begin{array}{r} 50 \\ \times\ 4 \\ \hline \end{array}$$

7.
$$\begin{array}{r} 30 \\ \times\ 6 \\ \hline \end{array}$$
$$\begin{array}{r} 20 \\ \times\ 6 \\ \hline \end{array}$$
$$\begin{array}{r} 90 \\ \times\ 6 \\ \hline \end{array}$$
$$\begin{array}{r} 70 \\ \times\ 9 \\ \hline \end{array}$$
$$\begin{array}{r} 40 \\ \times\ 7 \\ \hline \end{array}$$
$$\begin{array}{r} 60 \\ \times\ 4 \\ \hline \end{array}$$

Multiplication: Regrouping (III)

Name_____ Date_____

$$\begin{array}{r}9\mathbf{2}\\ \times\ \mathbf{4}\\ \hline 8\end{array}$$ First, multiply 2 ones by 4 ones.

$$\begin{array}{r}{}^3 9\mathbf{2}\\ \times\ \mathbf{4}\\ \hline \mathbf{6}8\end{array}$$ Then multiply 9 tens by 4 ones. Regroup the extra hundreds.

$$\begin{array}{r}{}^3 9\mathbf{2}\\ \times\ \mathbf{4}\\ \hline \mathbf{3}68\end{array}$$ Finally, add the hundreds.

Multiply.

1.
$$\begin{array}{r}53\\ \times 2\end{array}$$
$$\begin{array}{r}82\\ \times 4\end{array}$$
$$\begin{array}{r}43\\ \times 3\end{array}$$
$$\begin{array}{r}61\\ \times 2\end{array}$$
$$\begin{array}{r}74\\ \times 2\end{array}$$
$$\begin{array}{r}91\\ \times 7\end{array}$$

2.
$$\begin{array}{r}62\\ \times 4\end{array}$$
$$\begin{array}{r}51\\ \times 4\end{array}$$
$$\begin{array}{r}83\\ \times 3\end{array}$$
$$\begin{array}{r}72\\ \times 3\end{array}$$
$$\begin{array}{r}41\\ \times 5\end{array}$$
$$\begin{array}{r}32\\ \times 4\end{array}$$

3.
$$\begin{array}{r}53\\ \times 3\end{array}$$
$$\begin{array}{r}81\\ \times 8\end{array}$$
$$\begin{array}{r}42\\ \times 3\end{array}$$
$$\begin{array}{r}31\\ \times 9\end{array}$$
$$\begin{array}{r}63\\ \times 2\end{array}$$
$$\begin{array}{r}51\\ \times 6\end{array}$$

4.
$$\begin{array}{r}93\\ \times 2\end{array}$$
$$\begin{array}{r}61\\ \times 4\end{array}$$
$$\begin{array}{r}72\\ \times 4\end{array}$$
$$\begin{array}{r}52\\ \times 2\end{array}$$
$$\begin{array}{r}82\\ \times 2\end{array}$$
$$\begin{array}{r}93\\ \times 3\end{array}$$

5.
$$\begin{array}{r}31\\ \times 6\end{array}$$
$$\begin{array}{r}83\\ \times 2\end{array}$$
$$\begin{array}{r}92\\ \times 3\end{array}$$
$$\begin{array}{r}71\\ \times 8\end{array}$$
$$\begin{array}{r}62\\ \times 3\end{array}$$
$$\begin{array}{r}42\\ \times 4\end{array}$$

6.
$$\begin{array}{r}73\\ \times 3\end{array}$$
$$\begin{array}{r}61\\ \times 9\end{array}$$
$$\begin{array}{r}73\\ \times 2\end{array}$$
$$\begin{array}{r}54\\ \times 2\end{array}$$
$$\begin{array}{r}81\\ \times 7\end{array}$$
$$\begin{array}{r}64\\ \times 2\end{array}$$

7.
$$\begin{array}{r}82\\ \times 3\end{array}$$
$$\begin{array}{r}93\\ \times 3\end{array}$$
$$\begin{array}{r}61\\ \times 5\end{array}$$
$$\begin{array}{r}74\\ \times 2\end{array}$$
$$\begin{array}{r}91\\ \times 9\end{array}$$
$$\begin{array}{r}52\\ \times 4\end{array}$$

Unit 3

Name_____ Date_____

$\overset{2}{3}6$ First, multiply 6 ones
x 4 by 4 ones. Regroup
4 the extra tens.

$\overset{1\ 2}{3}6$ Then multiply 3 tens
x 4 by 4 ones. Add the
44 extra tens. Regroup
the extra hundreds.

$\overset{1\ 2}{3}6$ Finally, add
x 4 the hundreds.
144

Multiply.

1.
28	19	36	24	17	29
x 5	x 7	x 3	x 6	x 5	x 7

2.
32	35	33	23	22	28
x 7	x 4	x 8	x 9	x 6	x 6

3.
14	13	15	25	32	24
x 8	x 9	x 8	x 4	x 6	x 7

4.
37	39	18	27	28	26
x 4	x 7	x 8	x 5	x 4	x 8

5.
34	16	28	36	19	25
x 4	x 8	x 7	x 6	x 9	x 8

6.
12	22	14	33	13	27
x 9	x 7	x 9	x 5	x 8	x 7

7.
32	34	18	25	35	27
x 9	x 8	x 7	x 9	x 8	x 6

Name_____ Date_____

Unit 3

Multiply.

1. $\begin{array}{r} 63 \\ \times\ 5 \end{array}$ $\begin{array}{r} 52 \\ \times\ 7 \end{array}$ $\begin{array}{r} 86 \\ \times\ 3 \end{array}$ $\begin{array}{r} 74 \\ \times\ 3 \end{array}$ $\begin{array}{r} 48 \\ \times\ 3 \end{array}$ $\begin{array}{r} 93 \\ \times\ 6 \end{array}$

2. $\begin{array}{r} 38 \\ \times\ 4 \end{array}$ $\begin{array}{r} 77 \\ \times\ 2 \end{array}$ $\begin{array}{r} 59 \\ \times\ 3 \end{array}$ $\begin{array}{r} 64 \\ \times\ 4 \end{array}$ $\begin{array}{r} 46 \\ \times\ 4 \end{array}$ $\begin{array}{r} 89 \\ \times\ 2 \end{array}$

3. $\begin{array}{r} 37 \\ \times\ 6 \end{array}$ $\begin{array}{r} 55 \\ \times\ 5 \end{array}$ $\begin{array}{r} 84 \\ \times\ 4 \end{array}$ $\begin{array}{r} 93 \\ \times\ 5 \end{array}$ $\begin{array}{r} 42 \\ \times\ 8 \end{array}$ $\begin{array}{r} 56 \\ \times\ 7 \end{array}$

4. $\begin{array}{r} 73 \\ \times\ 9 \end{array}$ $\begin{array}{r} 64 \\ \times\ 7 \end{array}$ $\begin{array}{r} 85 \\ \times\ 4 \end{array}$ $\begin{array}{r} 39 \\ \times\ 3 \end{array}$ $\begin{array}{r} 88 \\ \times\ 6 \end{array}$ $\begin{array}{r} 59 \\ \times\ 7 \end{array}$

5. $\begin{array}{r} 72 \\ \times\ 5 \end{array}$ $\begin{array}{r} 94 \\ \times\ 9 \end{array}$ $\begin{array}{r} 58 \\ \times\ 7 \end{array}$ $\begin{array}{r} 47 \\ \times\ 5 \end{array}$ $\begin{array}{r} 67 \\ \times\ 6 \end{array}$ $\begin{array}{r} 87 \\ \times\ 8 \end{array}$

6. $\begin{array}{r} 45 \\ \times\ 6 \end{array}$ $\begin{array}{r} 54 \\ \times\ 4 \end{array}$ $\begin{array}{r} 85 \\ \times\ 3 \end{array}$ $\begin{array}{r} 76 \\ \times\ 8 \end{array}$ $\begin{array}{r} 68 \\ \times\ 7 \end{array}$ $\begin{array}{r} 52 \\ \times\ 9 \end{array}$

7. $\begin{array}{r} 63 \\ \times\ 8 \end{array}$ $\begin{array}{r} 37 \\ \times\ 9 \end{array}$ $\begin{array}{r} 69 \\ \times\ 4 \end{array}$ $\begin{array}{r} 57 \\ \times\ 3 \end{array}$ $\begin{array}{r} 46 \\ \times\ 9 \end{array}$ $\begin{array}{r} 74 \\ \times\ 8 \end{array}$

8. $\begin{array}{r} 86 \\ \times\ 5 \end{array}$ $\begin{array}{r} 44 \\ \times\ 3 \end{array}$ $\begin{array}{r} 53 \\ \times\ 6 \end{array}$ $\begin{array}{r} 75 \\ \times\ 9 \end{array}$ $\begin{array}{r} 64 \\ \times\ 8 \end{array}$ $\begin{array}{r} 98 \\ \times\ 7 \end{array}$

9. $\begin{array}{r} 56 \\ \times\ 4 \end{array}$ $\begin{array}{r} 43 \\ \times\ 9 \end{array}$ $\begin{array}{r} 87 \\ \times\ 4 \end{array}$ $\begin{array}{r} 96 \\ \times\ 6 \end{array}$ $\begin{array}{r} 79 \\ \times\ 4 \end{array}$ $\begin{array}{r} 67 \\ \times\ 3 \end{array}$

Name_____ Date_____

Read each problem then write an equation to solve it.

1. The diner has twelve tables that seat eight people each.
   How many people can be seated at these tables in all?

   ☐
   x ☐
   ☐

2. It has twenty-six booths that seat four people each.
   How many people can be seated at the booths in all?

   ☐
   x ☐
   ☐

3. If the diner serves sixty-eight burgers a day,
   how many burgers will be served in five days?

   ☐
   x ☐
   ☐

4. If the diner serves thirty-nine milkshakes a day,
   how many milkshakes will be served in three days?

   ☐
   x ☐
   ☐

5. If the diner serves forty-six bowls of soup a day,
   how many bowls of soup will be served in nine days?

   ☐
   x ☐
   ☐

6. A blue-plate special costs four dollars. How many
   dollars will thirty-five specials cost?

   ☐
   x ☐
   ☐

7. One waitress earns forty-seven dollars in tips a day.
   How many dollars will she earn in three days?

   ☐
   x ☐
   ☐

Name_____ Date_____

Unit 3

Multiply.

1.	6 x 6	7 x 8	9 x 3	8 x 6	6 x 9	7 x 5
2.	9 x 7	8 x 4	7 x 6	5 x 9	4 x 8	8 x 9
3.	12 x 3	10 x 5	11 x 7	12 x 4	11 x 6	10 x 3
4.	12 x 4	11 x 9	10 x 4	11 x 8	20 x 2	30 x 3
5.	31 x 3	42 x 2	24 x 2	32 x 3	22 x 4	41 x 2
6.	23 x 2	22 x 3	33 x 2	21 x 4	43 x 2	31 x 2
7.	60 x 4	90 x 8	30 x 7	40 x 5	80 x 9	50 x 8
8.	70 x 9	20 x 7	40 x 8	90 x 7	60 x 9	30 x 8
9.	52 x 3	64 x 2	71 x 5	36 x 2	42 x 4	91 x 7

Name_____ Date_____

1.
$$\begin{array}{r} 4 \\ \times\ 8 \\ \hline \end{array}$$
○ a) 28
○ b) 24
○ c) 36
○ d) 32

$$\begin{array}{r} 9 \\ \times\ 6 \\ \hline \end{array}$$
○ a) 54
○ b) 63
○ c) 56
○ d) 72

$$\begin{array}{r} 9 \\ \times\ 8 \\ \hline \end{array}$$
○ a) 64
○ b) 81
○ c) 72
○ d) 63

2.
$$\begin{array}{r} 10 \\ \times\ 7 \\ \hline \end{array}$$
○ a) 140
○ b) 70
○ c) 17
○ d) 35

$$\begin{array}{r} 40 \\ \times\ 2 \\ \hline \end{array}$$
○ a) 60
○ b) 20
○ c) 80
○ d) 90

$$\begin{array}{r} 32 \\ \times\ 3 \\ \hline \end{array}$$
○ a) 69
○ b) 94
○ c) 96
○ d) 66

3.
$$\begin{array}{r} 70 \\ \times\ 8 \\ \hline \end{array}$$
○ a) 540
○ b) 560
○ c) 720
○ d) 640

$$\begin{array}{r} 90 \\ \times\ 7 \\ \hline \end{array}$$
○ a) 720
○ b) 810
○ c) 630
○ d) 540

$$\begin{array}{r} 13 \\ \times\ 4 \\ \hline \end{array}$$
○ a) 52
○ b) 46
○ c) 42
○ d) 54

4.
$$\begin{array}{r} 31 \\ \times\ 6 \\ \hline \end{array}$$
○ a) 181
○ b) 161
○ c) 156
○ d) 186

$$\begin{array}{r} 62 \\ \times\ 3 \\ \hline \end{array}$$
○ a) 181
○ b) 246
○ c) 242
○ d) 186

$$\begin{array}{r} 96 \\ \times\ 5 \\ \hline \end{array}$$
○ a) 450
○ b) 485
○ c) 480
○ d) 460

5.
$$\begin{array}{r} 46 \\ \times\ 7 \\ \hline \end{array}$$
○ a) 322
○ b) 328
○ c) 288
○ d) 282

$$\begin{array}{r} 68 \\ \times\ 9 \\ \hline \end{array}$$
○ a) 632
○ b) 603
○ c) 622
○ d) 612

$$\begin{array}{r} 87 \\ \times\ 4 \\ \hline \end{array}$$
○ a) 328
○ b) 341
○ c) 348
○ d) 347

Division Terms

Division symbols
÷ or ⌐̄

Divisor
a number dividing another number

Dividend
a number being divided

Quotient
how many times a divisor divides or "goes into" a dividend

The equations below state that 8 divided by 4 equals 2.

$$8 \div 4 = 2$$
dividend **divisor** **quotient**

$$\overset{2 \leftarrow \text{quotient}}{\text{divisor} \rightarrow 4\overline{|8}} \leftarrow \text{dividend}$$

- -

Write the numbers in the correct spaces to complete what each equation states.

1. $5\overline{|15}$ (3)   _____ divided by _____ equals _____
   dividend   divisor   quotient

2. $21 \div 7 = 3$ _____ divided by _____ equals _____
   dividend   divisor   quotient

3. $3\overline{|12}$ (4)   _____ divided by _____ equals _____
   dividend   divisor   quotient

4. $32 \div 4 = 8$ _____ divided by _____ equals _____
   dividend   divisor   quotient

5. $2\overline{|10}$ (5)   _____ divided by _____ equals _____
   dividend   divisor   quotient

6. $18 \div 3 = 6$ _____ divided by _____ equals _____
   dividend   divisor   quotient

7. $7\overline{|14}$ (2)   _____ divided by _____ equals _____
   dividend   divisor   quotient

Division Practice (I)

Name_____ Date_____

$$\boxed{?}\,2\overline{)8} \;\rightarrow\; \text{THINK} \quad \begin{array}{r}\boxed{?}\\ \times\,2\\ \hline 8\end{array} \;\rightarrow\; \begin{array}{r}\boxed{4}\\ \times\,2\\ \hline 8\end{array} \;\rightarrow\; \text{therefore} \quad \boxed{4}\,2\overline{)8}$$

1.
$\boxed{} \rightarrow \boxed{}$
$\begin{array}{r}\times\,5\\ \hline 10\end{array}$ $5\overline{)10}$

2.
$\boxed{} \rightarrow \boxed{}$
$\begin{array}{r}\times\,4\\ \hline 16\end{array}$ $4\overline{)16}$

3.
$\boxed{} \rightarrow \boxed{}$
$\begin{array}{r}\times\,3\\ \hline 12\end{array}$ $3\overline{)12}$

4.
$\boxed{} \rightarrow \boxed{}$
$\begin{array}{r}\times\,6\\ \hline 24\end{array}$ $6\overline{)24}$

5.
$\boxed{} \rightarrow \boxed{}$
$\begin{array}{r}\times\,8\\ \hline 16\end{array}$ $8\overline{)16}$

6.
$\boxed{} \rightarrow \boxed{}$
$\begin{array}{r}\times\,5\\ \hline 15\end{array}$ $5\overline{)15}$

7.
$\boxed{} \rightarrow \boxed{}$
$\begin{array}{r}\times\,3\\ \hline 27\end{array}$ $3\overline{)27}$

8.
$\boxed{} \rightarrow \boxed{}$
$\begin{array}{r}\times\,9\\ \hline 36\end{array}$ $9\overline{)36}$

9.
$\boxed{} \rightarrow \boxed{}$
$\begin{array}{r}\times\,4\\ \hline 20\end{array}$ $4\overline{)20}$

10.
$\boxed{} \rightarrow \boxed{}$
$\begin{array}{r}\times\,7\\ \hline 28\end{array}$ $7\overline{)28}$

11.
$\boxed{} \rightarrow \boxed{}$
$\begin{array}{r}\times\,7\\ \hline 21\end{array}$ $7\overline{)21}$

12.
$\boxed{} \rightarrow \boxed{}$
$\begin{array}{r}\times\,9\\ \hline 45\end{array}$ $9\overline{)45}$

Name_____ Date_____

Zero cannot be a divisor because it has no value.

A number divided by one will always equal itself. $\dfrac{5}{1\overline{)5}}$

Zero divided by another number will always equal zero. $\dfrac{0}{4\overline{)0}}$

A number divided by itself will always equal one. $\dfrac{1}{5\overline{)5}}$

Divide.

1. $7\overline{)0}$ $9\overline{)9}$ $1\overline{)0}$ $8\overline{)8}$ $1\overline{)6}$ $5\overline{)0}$

2. $6\overline{)0}$ $1\overline{)1}$ $1\overline{)3}$ $9\overline{)0}$ $2\overline{)2}$ $2\overline{)0}$

3. $4\overline{)4}$ $1\overline{)5}$ $3\overline{)3}$ $8\overline{)0}$ $1\overline{)2}$ $1\overline{)9}$

4. $1\overline{)8}$ $7\overline{)7}$ $1\overline{)4}$ $3\overline{)0}$ $1\overline{)7}$ $6\overline{)6}$

Unit 4

Read each problem then write an equation to solve it.

5. Mrs. Morris made six cupcakes. She has six children and wants to divide them equally How many cupcakes will each child get?

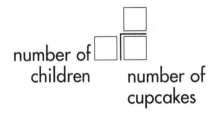

number of children   number of cupcakes

6. Mrs. Adams wants to cut one pie to serve five people, with none left over. How many slices should she cut?

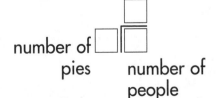

number of pies   number of people

Name_____ Date_____

Complete a partner multiplication fact to solve each division fact.

1.

$\square$ → $\square$
$\times\ 2$ $2\overline{)2}$
2

$\square$ → $\square$
$\times\ 2$ $2\overline{)4}$
4

$\square$ → $\square$
$\times\ 2$ $2\overline{)6}$
6

2.

$\square$ → $\square$
$\times\ 2$ $2\overline{)8}$
8

$\square$ → $\square$
$\times\ 2$ $2\overline{)10}$
10

$\square$ → $\square$
$\times\ 2$ $2\overline{)12}$
12

3.

$\square$ → $\square$
$\times\ 2$ $2\overline{)14}$
14

$\square$ → $\square$
$\times\ 2$ $2\overline{)16}$
16

$\square$ → $\square$
$\times\ 2$ $2\overline{)18}$
18

4.

$\square$ → $\square$
$\times\ 3$ $3\overline{)3}$
3

$\square$ → $\square$
$\times\ 3$ $3\overline{)6}$
6

$\square$ → $\square$
$\times\ 3$ $3\overline{)9}$
9

5.

$\square$ → $\square$
$\times\ 3$ $3\overline{)12}$
12

$\square$ → $\square$
$\times\ 3$ $3\overline{)15}$
15

$\square$ → $\square$
$\times\ 3$ $3\overline{)18}$
18

6.

$\square$ → $\square$
$\times\ 3$ $3\overline{)21}$
21

$\square$ → $\square$
$\times\ 3$ $3\overline{)24}$
24

$\square$ → $\square$
$\times\ 3$ $3\overline{)27}$
27

Divide.

7. $2\overline{)8}$ $3\overline{)3}$ $2\overline{)10}$ $3\overline{)24}$ $3\overline{)9}$ $2\overline{)14}$

8. $3\overline{)12}$ $2\overline{)6}$ $3\overline{)15}$ $2\overline{)16}$ $2\overline{)18}$ $3\overline{)21}$

9. $3\overline{)27}$ $2\overline{)4}$ $2\overline{)12}$ $3\overline{)6}$ $3\overline{)18}$ $2\overline{)2}$

Name_____ Date_____

Complete a partner multiplication fact to solve each division fact.

1. $\square$ → $\square$ $\quad$ $\begin{array}{r}\times\ 4\\ \hline 4\end{array}$ $\quad$ $4\overline{)4}$	$\square$ → $\square$ $\quad$ $\begin{array}{r}\times\ 4\\ \hline 8\end{array}$ $\quad$ $4\overline{)8}$	$\square$ → $\square$ $\quad$ $\begin{array}{r}\times\ 4\\ \hline 12\end{array}$ $\quad$ $4\overline{)12}$
2. $\square$ → $\square$ $\quad$ $\begin{array}{r}\times\ 4\\ \hline 16\end{array}$ $\quad$ $4\overline{)16}$	$\square$ → $\square$ $\quad$ $\begin{array}{r}\times\ 4\\ \hline 20\end{array}$ $\quad$ $4\overline{)20}$	$\square$ → $\square$ $\quad$ $\begin{array}{r}\times\ 4\\ \hline 24\end{array}$ $\quad$ $4\overline{)24}$
3. $\square$ → $\square$ $\quad$ $\begin{array}{r}\times\ 4\\ \hline 28\end{array}$ $\quad$ $4\overline{)28}$	$\square$ → $\square$ $\quad$ $\begin{array}{r}\times\ 4\\ \hline 32\end{array}$ $\quad$ $4\overline{)32}$	$\square$ → $\square$ $\quad$ $\begin{array}{r}\times\ 4\\ \hline 36\end{array}$ $\quad$ $4\overline{)36}$
4. $\square$ → $\square$ $\quad$ $\begin{array}{r}\times\ 5\\ \hline 5\end{array}$ $\quad$ $5\overline{)5}$	$\square$ → $\square$ $\quad$ $\begin{array}{r}\times\ 5\\ \hline 10\end{array}$ $\quad$ $5\overline{)10}$	$\square$ → $\square$ $\quad$ $\begin{array}{r}\times\ 5\\ \hline 15\end{array}$ $\quad$ $5\overline{)15}$
5. $\square$ → $\square$ $\quad$ $\begin{array}{r}\times\ 5\\ \hline 20\end{array}$ $\quad$ $5\overline{)20}$	$\square$ → $\square$ $\quad$ $\begin{array}{r}\times\ 5\\ \hline 25\end{array}$ $\quad$ $5\overline{)25}$	$\square$ → $\square$ $\quad$ $\begin{array}{r}\times\ 5\\ \hline 30\end{array}$ $\quad$ $5\overline{)30}$
6. $\square$ → $\square$ $\quad$ $\begin{array}{r}\times\ 5\\ \hline 35\end{array}$ $\quad$ $5\overline{)35}$	$\square$ → $\square$ $\quad$ $\begin{array}{r}\times\ 5\\ \hline 40\end{array}$ $\quad$ $5\overline{)40}$	$\square$ → $\square$ $\quad$ $\begin{array}{r}\times\ 5\\ \hline 45\end{array}$ $\quad$ $5\overline{)45}$

Unit 4

Divide.

7. $\quad 4\overline{)32} \qquad 5\overline{)20} \qquad 4\overline{)8} \qquad 5\overline{)5} \qquad 5\overline{)35} \qquad 4\overline{)12}$

8. $\quad 5\overline{)10} \qquad 4\overline{)28} \qquad 5\overline{)45} \qquad 4\overline{)20} \qquad 4\overline{)4} \qquad 5\overline{)15}$

9. $\quad 5\overline{)25} \qquad 1\overline{)4} \qquad 4\overline{)24} \qquad 5\overline{)40} \qquad 5\overline{)30} \qquad 4\overline{)36}$

Division Facts Drill (I)

Name_____ Date_____

Divide

1. $2\overline{)0}$ $5\overline{)5}$ $4\overline{)32}$ $3\overline{)18}$ $2\overline{)12}$ $4\overline{)4}$

2. $5\overline{)40}$ $3\overline{)27}$ $1\overline{)5}$ $3\overline{)0}$ $2\overline{)8}$ $4\overline{)24}$

3. $3\overline{)9}$ $5\overline{)15}$ $2\overline{)2}$ $4\overline{)12}$ $5\overline{)45}$ $3\overline{)21}$

4. $4\overline{)0}$ $4\overline{)16}$ $5\overline{)10}$ $3\overline{)3}$ $2\overline{)6}$ $3\overline{)24}$

5. $2\overline{)6}$ $5\overline{)0}$ $3\overline{)12}$ $5\overline{)35}$ $4\overline{)20}$ $3\overline{)6}$

6. $4\overline{)28}$ $2\overline{)10}$ $1\overline{)0}$ $2\overline{)18}$ $5\overline{)20}$ $1\overline{)2}$

7. $5\overline{)25}$ $1\overline{)3}$ $4\overline{)8}$ $3\overline{)15}$ $2\overline{)4}$ $1\overline{)1}$

8. $2\overline{)12}$ $4\overline{)36}$ $2\overline{)16}$ $1\overline{)4}$ $5\overline{)30}$ $2\overline{)14}$

Find the missing dividend.

9. $3\overline{)\boxed{}}^{\,6}$ $4\overline{)\boxed{}}^{\,9}$ $5\overline{)\boxed{}}^{\,4}$ $2\overline{)\boxed{}}^{\,7}$ $3\overline{)\boxed{}}^{\,5}$

10. $2\overline{)\boxed{}}^{\,9}$ $5\overline{)\boxed{}}^{\,8}$ $1\overline{)\boxed{}}^{\,2}$ $4\overline{)\boxed{}}^{\,6}$ $5\overline{)\boxed{}}^{\,9}$

Name_____ Date_____

Unit 4

Complete a partner multiplication fact to solve each division fact.

1.	$\square$ $\times 6$ / 6 → $\square$ / $6\overline{)6}$	$\square$ $\times 6$ / 12 → $\square$ / $6\overline{)12}$	$\square$ $\times 6$ / 18 → $\square$ / $6\overline{)18}$
2.	$\square$ $\times 6$ / 24 → $\square$ / $6\overline{)24}$	$\square$ $\times 6$ / 30 → $\square$ / $6\overline{)30}$	$\square$ $\times 6$ / 36 → $\square$ / $6\overline{)36}$
3.	$\square$ $\times 6$ / 42 → $\square$ / $6\overline{)42}$	$\square$ $\times 6$ / 48 → $\square$ / $6\overline{)48}$	$\square$ $\times 6$ / 54 → $\square$ / $6\overline{)54}$
4.	$\square$ $\times 7$ / 7 → $\square$ / $7\overline{)7}$	$\square$ $\times 7$ / 14 → $\square$ / $7\overline{)14}$	$\square$ $\times 7$ / 21 → $\square$ / $7\overline{)21}$
5.	$\square$ $\times 7$ / 28 → $\square$ / $7\overline{)28}$	$\square$ $\times 7$ / 35 → $\square$ / $7\overline{)35}$	$\square$ $\times 7$ / 42 → $\square$ / $7\overline{)42}$
6.	$\square$ $\times 7$ / 49 → $\square$ / $7\overline{)49}$	$\square$ $\times 7$ / 56 → $\square$ / $7\overline{)56}$	$\square$ $\times 7$ / 63 → $\square$ / $7\overline{)63}$

Divide.

7. $7\overline{)35}$ $6\overline{)18}$ $6\overline{)30}$ $7\overline{)7}$ $7\overline{)49}$ $6\overline{)42}$

8. $6\overline{)6}$ $7\overline{)14}$ $6\overline{)36}$ $7\overline{)28}$ $7\overline{)63}$ $6\overline{)48}$

9. $7\overline{)21}$ $6\overline{)24}$ $7\overline{)42}$ $6\overline{)12}$ $6\overline{)54}$ $7\overline{)56}$

Name_____ Date_____

Complete a partner multiplication fact to solve each division fact.

1.	□ → □ × 8 / 8 → 8)8	□ → □ × 8 / 16 → 8)16	□ → □ × 8 / 24 → 8)24
2.	□ → □ × 8 / 32 → 8)32	□ → □ × 8 / 40 → 8)40	□ → □ × 8 / 48 → 8)48
3.	□ → □ × 8 / 56 → 8)56	□ → □ × 8 / 64 → 8)64	□ → □ × 8 / 72 → 8)72
4.	□ → □ × 9 / 9 → 9)9	□ → □ × 9 / 18 → 9)18	□ → □ × 9 / 27 → 9)27
5.	□ → □ × 9 / 36 → 9)36	□ → □ × 9 / 45 → 9)45	□ → □ × 9 / 54 → 9)54
6.	□ → □ × 9 / 63 → 9)63	□ → □ × 9 / 72 → 9)72	□ → □ × 9 / 81 → 9)81

Divide.

7. 8)8   9)81   8)72   9)27   9)45   8)16

8. 9)63   8)64   9)9   8)24   8)56   9)18

9. 9)72   8)32   8)48   9)36   9)54   8)40

Name_____ Date_____

Divide.

1. $6\overline{)54}$	$9\overline{)45}$	$8\overline{)8}$	$7\overline{)35}$	$6\overline{)6}$	$8\overline{)24}$
2. $9\overline{)36}$	$7\overline{)21}$	$9\overline{)0}$	$7\overline{)63}$	$6\overline{)48}$	$8\overline{)40}$
3. $7\overline{)7}$	$9\overline{)27}$	$6\overline{)12}$	$8\overline{)56}$	$9\overline{)18}$	$7\overline{)49}$
4. $8\overline{)72}$	$8\overline{)16}$	$9\overline{)9}$	$7\overline{)14}$	$6\overline{)42}$	$8\overline{)32}$
5. $7\overline{)0}$	$9\overline{)81}$	$7\overline{)56}$	$9\overline{)54}$	$8\overline{)48}$	$7\overline{)28}$
6. $8\overline{)64}$	$6\overline{)36}$	$6\overline{)24}$	$9\overline{)63}$	$6\overline{)0}$	$6\overline{)18}$
7. $9\overline{)72}$	$1\overline{)7}$	$8\overline{)0}$	$7\overline{)42}$	$6\overline{)30}$	$1\overline{)1}$

Find the missing dividend.

8. $6\overline{)}\,^{6}$ $8\overline{)}\,^{9}$ $9\overline{)}\,^{2}$ $7\overline{)}\,^{7}$ $8\overline{)}\,^{5}$

9. $9\overline{)}\,^{3}$ $6\overline{)}\,^{8}$ $7\overline{)}\,^{6}$ $8\overline{)}\,^{4}$ $6\overline{)}\,^{9}$

10. $7\overline{)}\,^{9}$ $9\overline{)}\,^{8}$ $8\overline{)}\,^{3}$ $9\overline{)}\,^{9}$ $7\overline{)}\,^{4}$

Premium Education Math: Grade 3 **87**

Unit 4

Name_____ Date_____

Read each problem then write a division equation to solve it.

1. Thirty-two students in art class are split into groups of four. How many groups are formed?

2. Twenty-eight students in gym class are split into groups of four. How many groups are formed?

3. There are seventy-two students in the cafeteria. Eight students sit at each table. How many tables are used?

4. The cafeteria sells cookies for five cents each. Jo has thirty cents. How many cookies can she buy?

5. Mrs. Guadiz reads nine pages of a fifty-four page book to her class each day. How many days will it take to finish the book?

6. Seth wrote four pages of his thirty-six page science report each day. How many days did it take him to finish it?

7. There are forty-two days left in the school year. How many full weeks of school are left?

Name_____ Date_____

Divide.

1. $8\overline{)48}$ $9\overline{)63}$ $8\overline{)56}$ $6\overline{)18}$ $6\overline{)24}$ $7\overline{)63}$

2. $5\overline{)45}$ $8\overline{)24}$ $6\overline{)42}$ $8\overline{)16}$ $3\overline{)21}$ $9\overline{)18}$

3. $2\overline{)8}$ $9\overline{)72}$ $5\overline{)0}$ $7\overline{)14}$ $5\overline{)35}$ $9\overline{)54}$

4. $6\overline{)36}$ $8\overline{)40}$ $2\overline{)14}$ $4\overline{)12}$ $6\overline{)42}$ $5\overline{)20}$

5. $1\overline{)9}$ $5\overline{)15}$ $3\overline{)18}$ $9\overline{)81}$ $7\overline{)56}$ $4\overline{)32}$

6. $5\overline{)25}$ $3\overline{)0}$ $6\overline{)30}$ $7\overline{)49}$ $9\overline{)45}$ $6\overline{)54}$

7. $3\overline{)12}$ $5\overline{)10}$ $6\overline{)6}$ $5\overline{)40}$ $7\overline{)42}$ $4\overline{)28}$

8. $6\overline{)12}$ $8\overline{)8}$ $1\overline{)4}$ $8\overline{)64}$ $3\overline{)24}$ $5\overline{)5}$

9. $2\overline{)12}$ $8\overline{)72}$ $7\overline{)7}$ $9\overline{)27}$ $8\overline{)32}$ $4\overline{)24}$

10. $4\overline{)0}$ $9\overline{)36}$ $7\overline{)35}$ $4\overline{)20}$ $3\overline{)9}$ $4\overline{)16}$

Unit 4

Name_____ Date_____

Read each problem then write a division equation to solve it.

1. Nine bags of grass seed weigh seventy-two pounds altogether. How many pounds does each bag weigh?

2. Eight boxes of nails weigh twenty-four pounds altogether. How many pounds does each box weigh?

3. Five cases of golf balls weigh thirty pounds altogether. How many pounds does each case weigh?

4. Seven bags of gumballs weigh fifty-six ounces altogether. How many ounces does each bag weigh?

5. Six bottles of oil hold forty-eight ounces altogether. How many ounces does each bottle hold?

6. Three sacks of salt weigh twenty-seven pounds altogether. How many pounds does each sack weigh?

7. Four bottles of juice hold thirty-six ounces altogether. How many ounces does each bottle hold?

Name_____ Date_____

Find the missing dividend.

1. $7\overline{)}^{6}$ $9\overline{)}^{6}$ $8\overline{)}^{9}$ $2\overline{)}^{7}$ $4\overline{)}^{7}$ $8\overline{)}^{8}$

2. $6\overline{)}^{2}$ $5\overline{)}^{7}$ $3\overline{)}^{9}$ $8\overline{)}^{7}$ $7\overline{)}^{7}$ $7\overline{)}^{9}$

3. $2\overline{)}^{6}$ $3\overline{)}^{3}$ $8\overline{)}^{5}$ $8\overline{)}^{6}$ $7\overline{)}^{3}$ $9\overline{)}^{4}$

4. $5\overline{)}^{5}$ $7\overline{)}^{0}$ $3\overline{)}^{4}$ $4\overline{)}^{6}$ $7\overline{)}^{4}$ $9\overline{)}^{3}$

Unit 4

Find the missing divisor.

5. $\square\overline{)15}^{5}$ $\square\overline{)48}^{8}$ $\square\overline{)32}^{4}$ $\square\overline{)36}^{6}$ $\square\overline{)24}^{4}$ $\square\overline{)45}^{9}$

6. $\square\overline{)16}^{4}$ $\square\overline{)35}^{7}$ $\square\overline{)54}^{9}$ $\square\overline{)63}^{7}$ $\square\overline{)25}^{5}$ $\square\overline{)40}^{8}$

7. $\square\overline{)10}^{2}$ $\square\overline{)21}^{3}$ $\square\overline{)14}^{7}$ $\square\overline{)64}^{8}$ $\square\overline{)27}^{3}$ $\square\overline{)81}^{9}$

8. $\square\overline{)20}^{4}$ $\square\overline{)16}^{.8}$ $\square\overline{)3}^{3}$ $\square\overline{)72}^{9}$ $\square\overline{)42}^{7}$ $\square\overline{)30}^{6}$

Name_____ Date_____

Fill in the circle next to the correct product.

1. $4\overline{)24}$
   - a) 6
   - b) 4
   - c) 8
   - d) 7

   $6\overline{)48}$
   - a) 6
   - b) 7
   - c) 8
   - d) 5

   $7\overline{)42}$
   - a) 4
   - b) 8
   - c) 6
   - d) 7

2. $3\overline{)27}$
   - a) 7
   - b) 6
   - c) 9
   - d) 8

   $6\overline{)42}$
   - a) 7
   - b) 8
   - c) 6
   - d) 9

   $5\overline{)15}$
   - a) 4
   - b) 3
   - c) 5
   - d) 2

3. $9\overline{)81}$
   - a) 7
   - b) 9
   - c) 8
   - d) 6

   $7\overline{)63}$
   - a) 5
   - b) 7
   - c) 8
   - d) 9

   $8\overline{)64}$
   - a) 6
   - b) 8
   - c) 5
   - d) 7

4. $6\overline{)36}$
   - a) 5
   - b) 4
   - c) 8
   - d) 6

   $9\overline{)27}$
   - a) 4
   - b) 5
   - c) 3
   - d) 2

   $7\overline{)49}$
   - a) 9
   - b) 7
   - c) 6
   - d) 8

5. $6\overline{)54}$
   - a) 9
   - b) 6
   - c) 8
   - d) 7

   $9\overline{)45}$
   - a) 6
   - b) 5
   - c) 4
   - d) 7

   $8\overline{)72}$
   - a) 7
   - b) 8
   - c) 6
   - d) 9

6. $7\overline{)35}$
   - a) 4
   - b) 3
   - c) 5
   - d) 6

   $6\overline{)24}$
   - a) 8
   - b) 4
   - c) 6
   - d) 7

   $7\overline{)28}$
   - a) 3
   - b) 5
   - c) 4
   - d) 6

7. $3\overline{)12}$
   - a) 2
   - b) 3
   - c) 4
   - d) 5

   $2\overline{)18}$
   - a) 6
   - b) 9
   - c) 8
   - d) 7

   $8\overline{)24}$
   - a) 4
   - b) 5
   - c) 6
   - d) 3

Division Review (II)

Name_____ Date_____

Read each problem then write an equation to solve it.

1. There are four paws per kitten and thirty-two paws in all. How many kittens are there?
   ○ a) 6   ○ b) 8   ○ c) 9   ○ d) 4

2. There are thirty puppy treats and six puppies. How many treats does each puppy get?
   ○ a) 6   ○ b) 8   ○ c) 3   ○ d) 5

3. There are eight fish per tank and fifty-six fish in all. How many tanks are there?
   ○ a) 9   ○ b) 6   ○ c) 5   ○ d) 7

4. Each turtle lays three eggs. There are twenty-seven eggs in all. How many turtles laid the eggs?
   ○ a) 9   ○ b) 8   ○ c) 7   ○ d) 6

5. Each chimp eats five bananas. Forty-five bananas are eaten in all. How many chimps are there?
   ○ a) 7   ○ b) 9   ○ c) 8   ○ d) 5

6. Each lizard eats nine flies for breakfast. A total of seventy-two flies are eaten. How many lizards are there?
   ○ a) 7   ○ b) 9   ○ c) 8   ○ d) 6

7. Six hermit crabs cost eighteen dollars. How many dollars does each crab cost?
   ○ a) 4   ○ b) 5   ○ c) 2   ○ d) 3

Unit 4

Name_____ Date_____

A fraction is a part of a whole.
This whole is divided into 2 equal parts.
The shaded part is 1 part of the whole.

$\dfrac{1}{2}$ → shaded part of the whole
→ equal parts in one whole

- -

Color one part of each whole and write how many parts you colored. Then write how many parts are in the whole.

1. ☐ ← equal parts colored
   ☐ ← parts in one whole

2. ☐ ← equal parts colored
   ☐ ← parts in one whole

3. ☐ ← equal parts colored
   ☐ ← parts in one whole

4. ☐ ← equal parts colored
   ☐ ← parts in one whole

5. ☐ ← equal parts colored
   ☐ ← parts in one whole

6. ☐ ← equal parts colored
   ☐ ← parts in one whole

7. ☐ ← equal parts colored
   ☐ ← parts in one whole

8. ☐ ← equal parts colored
   ☐ ← parts in one whole

9. ☐ ← equal parts colored
   ☐ ← parts in one whole

10. ☐ ← equal parts colored
    ☐ ← parts in one whole

Fraction Terms (II)

Name_____ Date_____

A fraction has two parts—a numerator and a denominator.
The numerator is written above a bar.
The denominator is written below that bar.

$$\frac{\text{numerator}}{\text{denominator}}$$ → The number that shows the parts being counted.
→ The number that shows the total parts in the whole.

Count the shaded parts and write the numerator. Then count the total number of parts and write the denominator.

Unit 4

1.  numerator → ☐
denominator → ☐

2.  numerator → ☐
denominator → ☐

3.   numerator → ☐
denominator → ☐

4. 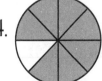 numerator → ☐
denominator → ☐

5.  numerator → ☐
denominator → ☐

6. 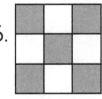 numerator → ☐
denominator → ☐

7.   numerator → ☐
denominator → ☐

8. 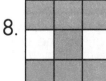 numerator → ☐
denominator → ☐

9.  numerator → ☐
denominator → ☐

10.   numerator → ☐
denominator → ☐

Name_____ Date_____

$\frac{1}{2}$	$\frac{1}{3}$	$\frac{2}{3}$	$\frac{1}{4}$	$\frac{2}{4}$	$\frac{3}{4}$
one half	one third	two thirds	one fourth	two-fourths	three-fourths

Write the fraction for each shaded area in number and in word form.

1. 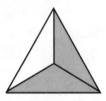 $\frac{1}{2}$ one half

2. 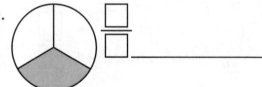 $\frac{\square}{\square}$ _____

3.  $\frac{\square}{\square}$ _____

4. 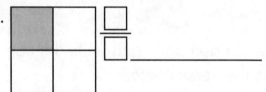 $\frac{\square}{\square}$ _____

5. $\frac{\square}{\square}$ _____

6. 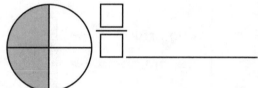 $\frac{\square}{\square}$ _____

7.  $\frac{\square}{\square}$ _____

8. 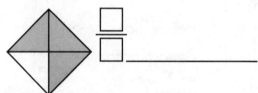 $\frac{\square}{\square}$ _____

Read each problem and circle the correct answer.

9. A pie is cut into four pieces. Sue eats two pieces. How much of the pie did Sue eat? $\frac{2}{3}$ $\frac{1}{4}$ $\frac{2}{4}$

10. Joe has three rocks. Two are white and one is gray. What fraction of the rocks is gray? $\frac{1}{3}$ $\frac{2}{3}$ $\frac{3}{4}$

Fractions (II)

Name_____ Date_____

When a whole number is divided into equal parts, each of those parts is a fraction of the whole number.

In the problem below, the divisor 3 becomes the denominator of the fraction.

$$12 \div 3 = 4 \quad \text{therefore} \quad \frac{1}{3} \text{ of } 12 = 4$$

Solve each division problem. Use the divisor to complete the fraction and the quotient to complete the fact sentence.

1. $10 \div 2 = \square$ so $\dfrac{1}{\square}$ of $10 = \square$

2. $15 \div 3 = \square$ so $\dfrac{1}{\square}$ of $15 = \square$

3. $24 \div 4 = \square$ so $\dfrac{1}{\square}$ of $24 = \square$

4. $16 \div 2 = \square$ so $\dfrac{1}{\square}$ of $16 = \square$

5. $27 \div 3 = \square$ so $\dfrac{1}{\square}$ of $27 = \square$

6. $36 \div 4 = \square$ so $\dfrac{1}{\square}$ of $36 = \square$

7. $21 \div 3 = \square$ so $\dfrac{1}{\square}$ of $21 = \square$

8. $8 \div 2 = \square$ so $\dfrac{1}{\square}$ of $8 = \square$

9. $12 \div 4 = \square$ so $\dfrac{1}{\square}$ of $12 = \square$

10. $18 \div 3 = \square$ so $\dfrac{1}{\square}$ of $18 = \square$

Unit 4

Fractions (III)

Name_____ Date_____

$\dfrac{1}{5}$ one fifth $\dfrac{1}{6}$ one sixth $\dfrac{1}{7}$ one seventh

$\dfrac{2}{5}$ two fifths $\dfrac{2}{6}$ two sixths $\dfrac{2}{7}$ two sevenths

Write the fraction for each shaded area in number and in word form.

1. $\dfrac{4}{5}$ four fifths

2. 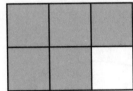 $\dfrac{\square}{\square}$ _____

3. 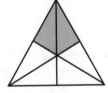 $\dfrac{\square}{\square}$ _____

4. 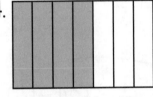 $\dfrac{\square}{\square}$ _____

5. 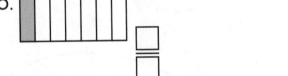 $\dfrac{\square}{\square}$ _____

6. $\dfrac{\square}{\square}$ _____

7. $\dfrac{\square}{\square}$ _____

8. $\dfrac{\square}{\square}$ _____

Read each problem and circle the correct answer.

9. It rained three days last week. What fraction of the week did it rain? $\dfrac{4}{7}$ $\dfrac{3}{7}$ $\dfrac{2}{7}$

10. Out of five children, three have chicken pox. What fraction of children has chicken pox? $\dfrac{5}{7}$ $\dfrac{3}{4}$ $\dfrac{3}{5}$

Fractions (IV)

Name_____ Date_____

$\dfrac{1}{8}$ one eighth $\dfrac{1}{9}$ one ninth $\dfrac{1}{10}$ one tenth

$\dfrac{2}{8}$ two eighths $\dfrac{2}{9}$ two ninths $\dfrac{2}{10}$ two tenths

Write the fraction for each shaded area in number and in word form.

1.

$\dfrac{1}{8}$ one eighth

2.

$\dfrac{}{}$ _____

3.
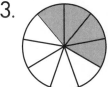
$\dfrac{}{}$ _____

4.
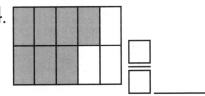
$\dfrac{}{}$ _____

5.

$\dfrac{}{}$ _____

6.

$\dfrac{}{}$ _____

7.

$\dfrac{}{}$ _____

8.

$\dfrac{}{}$ _____

Read each problem and circle the correct answer.

9. Eight students took a test. Three received an A.
What fraction of the students received an A? $\dfrac{3}{8}$ $\dfrac{5}{8}$ $\dfrac{3}{5}$

10. Out of ten students, seven walk to school.
What fraction of students walks to school? $\dfrac{3}{7}$ $\dfrac{7}{10}$ $\dfrac{7}{8}$

Fractions (V)

Name_____ Date_____

Solve each division problem. Use the divisor to complete the fraction and the quotient to complete the fact sentence.

1. $81 \div 9 = \square$ so $\dfrac{1}{\square}$ of 81 = $\square$

2. $72 \div 8 = \square$ so $\dfrac{1}{\square}$ of 72 = $\square$

3. $49 \div 7 = \square$ so $\dfrac{1}{\square}$ of 49 = $\square$

4. $18 \div 6 = \square$ so $\dfrac{1}{\square}$ of 18 = $\square$

5. $42 \div 6 = \square$ so $\dfrac{1}{\square}$ of 42 = $\square$

6. $20 \div 5 = \square$ so $\dfrac{1}{\square}$ of 20 = $\square$

7. $45 \div 9 = \square$ so $\dfrac{1}{\square}$ of 45 = $\square$

8. $54 \div 6 = \square$ so $\dfrac{1}{\square}$ of 54 = $\square$

9. $63 \div 7 = \square$ so $\dfrac{1}{\square}$ of 63 = $\square$

10. $56 \div 7 = \square$ so $\dfrac{1}{\square}$ of 56 = $\square$

Fractions Review

Name_____ Date_____

Fill in the circle next to the correct fraction.

1. Six out of seven cupcakes have white frosting. What fraction of cupcakes has white frosting?

   ○ a) $\frac{3}{7}$ ○ b) $\frac{1}{7}$ ○ c) $\frac{6}{7}$ ○ d) $\frac{1}{6}$

2. Nine pies were baked. Five have apple filling. What fraction of pies does not have apple filling?

   ○ a) $\frac{5}{9}$ ○ b) $\frac{4}{9}$ ○ c) $\frac{3}{9}$ ○ d) $\frac{4}{5}$

3. Five batches of cookies burned. Two batches did not. What fraction of cookies burned?

   ○ a) $\frac{2}{7}$ ○ b) $\frac{2}{5}$ ○ c) $\frac{5}{7}$ ○ d) $\frac{1}{5}$

4. Eight cakes were baked. Three are chocolate. What fraction of cakes is not chocolate?

   ○ a) $\frac{5}{8}$ ○ b) $\frac{1}{8}$ ○ c) $\frac{3}{8}$ ○ d) $\frac{3}{5}$

5. There are ten donuts on a tray. Four have sprinkles. What fraction of donuts has sprinkles?

   ○ a) $\frac{4}{6}$ ○ b) $\frac{6}{10}$ ○ c) $\frac{1}{4}$ ○ d) $\frac{4}{10}$

6. Seven danish have icing. Two do not. What fraction of danish has icing?

   ○ a) $\frac{2}{9}$ ○ b) $\frac{7}{9}$ ○ c) $\frac{2}{7}$ ○ d) $\frac{1}{9}$

7. Four loaves of bread have poppy seeds. Three do not. What fraction of bread has poppy seeds?

   ○ a) $\frac{1}{4}$ ○ b) $\frac{3}{4}$ ○ c) $\frac{3}{7}$ ○ d) $\frac{4}{7}$

Unit 4

Money Terms

Name_____ Date_____

Cents are equal parts of a whole dollar. Cents are written as decimal fractions, or decimals. A dollar has the value of 100 cents.

$$\$1.00 = \text{one whole dollar} = 100¢$$

The decimal point is placed after the whole dollar amount and before the cents.

12 whole dollars   36 cents of one whole dollar

$12.36

decimal point

1. Three dollars, fifteen cents $3.15

2. Four dollars, twenty cents   _____

3. Five dollars, fifty-two cents   _____

4. Ten dollars, sixty-five cents   _____

5. Two dollars, twelve cents   _____

6. Fifteen dollars   _____

7. Seven dollars, ten cents   _____

8. Twenty dollars, thirty cents   _____

9. Twelve dollars, eleven cents   _____

10. Forty-two dollars, forty cents   _____

11. Sixteen dollars, fifty cents   _____

12. Sixty dollars, fifty-five cents   _____

13. One dollar, sixty-three cents   _____

14. Six dollars, ninety-nine cents   _____

15. Eleven dollars, ninety cents   _____

16. Ninety dollars, eighteen cents   _____

Money: Decimals and Fractions

Name_____ Date_____

$.10 = \dfrac{1}{10}$ = one tenth $\qquad$ $.01 = \dfrac{1}{100}$ = one hundredth

64¢ or $0.64 = $\dfrac{6}{10} + \dfrac{4}{100}$ or six tenths plus four hundredths of a dollar

$2.05 = two dollars plus $\dfrac{5}{100}$ or five hundreths of a dollar

Write each value in decimal number form.

1. three tenths plus two hundredths of a dollar $\qquad$ _$0.32_

2. seven tenths plus five hundredths of a dollar $\qquad$ _____

3. eight tenths plus one hundredth of a dollar $\qquad$ _____

4. nine tenths of a dollar $\qquad$ _____

5. two tenths plus nine hundredths of a dollar $\qquad$ _____

6. $\dfrac{5}{10} + \dfrac{3}{100}$ of a dollar $\qquad$ _____

7. $\dfrac{7}{10}$ of a dollar $\qquad$ _____

8. two dollars plus $\dfrac{4}{10}$ of a dollar $\qquad$ _____

9. four dollars plus $\dfrac{1}{100}$ of a dollar $\qquad$ _____

10. five dollars plus six tenths of a dollar $\qquad$ _____

11. ten dollars plus $\dfrac{1}{10}$ of a dollar $\qquad$ _____

12. one dollar plus nine hundredths of a dollar $\qquad$ _____

Unit 4

Money: Addition and Subtraction

Name_____ Date_____

To add or subtract money values,
first line up the decimal points.
Bring the decimal point down
in the same place for the sum or difference.

$$\begin{array}{r} \$2.03 \\ +\ \$1.64 \\ \hline \$3.67 \end{array} \qquad \begin{array}{r} \$5.98 \\ -\ \$0.23 \\ \hline \$5.75 \end{array}$$

Add.

1.
$$\begin{array}{r} \$1.00 \\ +\ \$0.45 \end{array} \qquad \begin{array}{r} \$4.42 \\ +\ \$0.23 \end{array} \qquad \begin{array}{r} \$6.05 \\ +\ \$0.14 \end{array} \qquad \begin{array}{r} \$7.72 \\ +\ \$2.25 \end{array} \qquad \begin{array}{r} \$3.31 \\ +\ \$4.67 \end{array}$$

2.
$$\begin{array}{r} \$8.54 \\ +\ \$0.12 \end{array} \qquad \begin{array}{r} \$7.36 \\ +\ \$0.28 \end{array} \qquad \begin{array}{r} \$5.62 \\ +\ \$0.68 \end{array} \qquad \begin{array}{r} \$2.06 \\ +\ \$0.97 \end{array} \qquad \begin{array}{r} \$4.87 \\ +\ \$1.23 \end{array}$$

3.
$$\begin{array}{r} \$6.78 \\ +\ \$2.34 \end{array} \qquad \begin{array}{r} \$5.55 \\ +\ \$3.29 \end{array} \qquad \begin{array}{r} \$1.89 \\ +\ \$6.99 \end{array} \qquad \begin{array}{r} \$3.50 \\ +\ \$4.55 \end{array} \qquad \begin{array}{r} \$4.39 \\ +\ \$6.75 \end{array}$$

Subtract.

4.
$$\begin{array}{r} \$2.35 \\ -\ \$0.20 \end{array} \qquad \begin{array}{r} \$6.78 \\ -\ \$0.42 \end{array} \qquad \begin{array}{r} \$9.57 \\ -\ \$0.17 \end{array} \qquad \begin{array}{r} \$3.45 \\ -\ \$1.25 \end{array} \qquad \begin{array}{r} \$7.84 \\ -\ \$2.22 \end{array}$$

5.
$$\begin{array}{r} \$3.98 \\ -\ \$0.57 \end{array} \qquad \begin{array}{r} \$6.90 \\ -\ \$0.55 \end{array} \qquad \begin{array}{r} \$9.35 \\ -\ \$0.79 \end{array} \qquad \begin{array}{r} \$2.48 \\ -\ \$1.39 \end{array} \qquad \begin{array}{r} \$5.00 \\ -\ \$2.49 \end{array}$$

6.
$$\begin{array}{r} \$7.05 \\ -\ \$3.98 \end{array} \qquad \begin{array}{r} \$8.42 \\ -\ \$6.53 \end{array} \qquad \begin{array}{r} \$9.00 \\ -\ \$8.19 \end{array} \qquad \begin{array}{r} \$4.19 \\ -\ \$2.99 \end{array} \qquad \begin{array}{r} \$8.64 \\ -\ \$6.98 \end{array}$$

Money Word Problems (I)

Name_____ Date_____

Read each problem then write an equation to solve it. Circle **A** if you added to solve it. Circle **S** if you subtracted.

1. If milk costs $1.98 and eggs cost 89¢, how does it cost to buy both milk and eggs?

    +/− **A** **S**

2. Mrs. Alvarez spent $3.98 on groceries and paid with a $5 bill. How much change did she receive?

    +/− **A** **S**

3. Mr. Bly's groceries cost $6.42, but he has coupons worth 75¢. How much will he save if he uses the coupons?

    +/− **A** **S**

4. Mrs. Lee spent $9.45 on groceries. If she had used her coupons, she would have only spent $7.20. How much would she have saved?

    +/− **A** **S**

5. Ann bought lollipops for $1.79 and chocolate bars for $2.95. How much did she spend?

    +/− **A** **S**

6. Hot dogs are on sale for $1.59 a package. They normally cost $2.25. How much less do they cost on sale?

    +/− **A** **S**

7. Cartons of juice are sold two for $4.00 or one for $2.39. How much will three cost?

    +/− **A** **S**

Unit 4

Money Word Problems (II)

Name_____ Date_____

Use the movie theatre cost chart to solve each problem. Fill in the circle next to the correct answer.

Adult tickets $5.00	Large popcorn $4.50	Candy $2.25
Child tickets $3.25	Small popcorn $2.50	Soda $2.50

1. How much will it cost for Mr. Ling to see a movie and buy a small popcorn?

   ○ a) $8.75   ○ b) $7.50   ○ c) $9.50   ○ d) $8.25

2. How much does it cost for a soda and two boxes of candy?

   ○ a) $ 6.75   ○ b) $7.25   ○ c) $7.00   ○ d) $8.00

3. How much does it cost for two small popcorns and one box of candy?

   ○ a) $7.25   ○ b) $9.75   ○ c) $11.25   ○ d) $7.75

4. Mrs. Antonelli paid for one adult ticket and one child ticket with a $10 bill. How much change did she receive?

   ○ a) $1.25   ○ b) $1.50   ○ c) $2.75   ○ d) $1.75

5. How much does one large popcorn and two sodas cost?

   ○ a) $10.50   ○ b) $11.50   ○ c) $9.50   ○ d) $12.50

6. Peter, who is 9 years old, has $9.50 to spend at the movies. After he buys his ticket, how much will Peter have left over for snacks?

   ○ a) $5.25   ○ b) $7.25   ○ c) $6.25   ○ d) $6.75

U.S. Customary Units of Length (I)

Name_____ Date_____

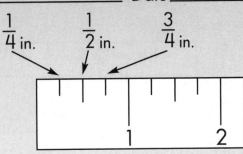

Length can be measured in inches.

inch = in.

- -

Use a ruler to measure the length of each line.

1. _____   _____ in.

2. _____   _____ in.

3. _____   _____ in.

4. _____   _____ in.

5. _____   _____ in.

Use a ruler to draw a line for each measurement.

6. $\frac{1}{2}$ in.   7. $1\frac{1}{4}$ in.

8. $4\frac{1}{2}$ in.

9. $5\frac{3}{4}$ in.

10. $3\frac{1}{4}$ in.

11. $2\frac{1}{2}$ in.

U.S. Customary Units of Length (II)

Name_____ Date_____

foot = ft.
yard = yd.

| 1 ft. = 12 in. | 1 yd. = 3 ft. | 1 yd. = 36 in. |

Find the equivalent measurement.

1. 12 in. = _____ ft.   36 in. = _____ yd.   24 in. = _____ ft.

2. 36 in. = _____ ft.   2 yd. = _____ ft.   15 ft. = _____ yd.

3. 4 yd. = _____ ft.   3 yd. = _____ in.   30 ft. = _____ yd.

4. 7 ft. = _____ in.   45 ft. = _____ yd.   12 ft. = _____ in.

5. 4 yd. = _____ in.   20 yd. = _____ ft.   50 yd. = _____ ft.

Solve each problem.

6. Sal is 5 feet tall. What is his height in inches? _____

7. Bob ran 12 yards. What is the distance? _____

8. Amy has 6 feet of fabric.
    How much fabric does she have in inches? _____

9. Sue's pool is 24 feet wide.
    What is the width in yards? _____

10. Both Lia and Jamie are 4 feet 6 inches tall.
    What is their combined height in yards? _____

U.S. Customary Units of Weight

Name_____ Date_____

about one ounce or 1 oz.

about one pound or 1 lb.

about one ton or 1 T.

16 oz. = 1 lb.   2,000 lbs. = 1 T.

Circle the correct unit of measurement used to measure the weight of each.

1.   lbs.   oz.
2.   lbs.   oz.
3.   lbs.   oz.
4. lbs.   oz.
5.  lbs.   oz.
6. lbs.   oz.
7.  lbs.   oz.
8. lbs.   oz.

Find the equivalent measurement.

9. 1 lb.= _____ oz.

10. 2 lbs. = _____ oz.

11. 1 $\frac{1}{2}$ lbs. = _____ oz.

12. 1 T. = _____ lbs.

13. $\frac{1}{2}$ T. = _____ lbs.

14. 64 oz. = _____ lbs.

5. 32 oz. = _____ lbs.

16. 10 lbs. = _____ oz.

17. 5 T. = _____ lbs.

18. 6 lbs. = _____ oz.

19. 3 $\frac{1}{2}$ lbs. = _____ oz.

20. 4,000 lbs. = _____T.

U.S. Customary Units of Liquid Volume

Name_____ Date_____

| 2 cups = 1 pint |
| 2 pints = 1 quart |
| 4 quarts = 1 gallon |

8 liquid ounces or 8 oz. = 1 cup
16 liquid ounces or 16 oz. = 1 pint
32 liquid ounces or 32 oz. = 1 quart
128 liquid ounces or 128 oz. = 1 gallon

Circle the correct unit of measurement used to measure the capacity of each.

1. **bath tub**   cups   quarts
   pints   gallons

2. **coffee mug**   cups   quarts
   pints   gallons

3. **soda can**   cups   quarts
   pints   gallons

4. **teapot**   cup   quarts
   pints   gallons

5. **ice cube tray**   cups   quarts
   pints   gallons

6. **large bottle of soda**   cups   quarts
   pints   gallons

Find the equivalent measurement.

7. 2 cups = _____ pint

8. 4 pints = _____ quarts

9. 8 quarts = _____ gallons

10. 1 pint = _____ oz.

11. 2 quarts = _____ oz.

12. 6 cups = _____ pints

13. 2 gallons = _____ oz.

14. 10 pints = _____ quarts

15. 3 quarts = _____ oz.

16. 16 quarts = _____ gallons

17. 4 cups = _____ oz.

18. 4 quarts = _____ oz.

19. 1 gallon = _____ cups

20. 24 quarts = _____ gallons

21. 5 quarts = _____ oz.

22. 32 pints = _____ gallons

Measurement Review (I)

Name_____ Date_____

Fill in the circle next to the correct answer.

1. A cup measures _____.
   - ○ a) length
   - ○ b) liquid volume
   - ○ c) time
   - ○ d) weight

2. An inch measures _____.
   - ○ a) length
   - ○ b) liquid volume
   - ○ c) time
   - ○ d) weight

3. An ounce can measure _____.
   - ○ a) length
   - ○ b) yards
   - ○ c) time
   - ○ d) weight

4. Which unit does not measure liquid volume?
   - ○ a) cup
   - ○ b) pound
   - ○ c) pint
   - ○ d) gallon

5. Which unit does not measure length?
   - ○ a) yard
   - ○ b) foot
   - ○ c) pound
   - ○ d) inch

6. Which unit does not measure weight?
   - ○ a) gallon
   - ○ b) ounce
   - ○ c) ton
   - ○ d) pound

7. 128 liquid oz. =
   - ○ a) 3 pints
   - ○ b) 6 cups
   - ○ c) 2 quarts
   - ○ d) 1 gallon

8. 3 yd. =
   - ○ a) 108 in.
   - ○ b) 120 in.
   - ○ c) 96 in.
   - ○ d) 132 in.

9. 6 lbs. =
   - ○ a) 72 oz.
   - ○ b) 64 oz.
   - ○ c) 48 oz.
   - ○ d) 96 oz.

10. 8 pints does not equal
   - ○ a) 16 cups
   - ○ b) 1 gallon
   - ○ c) 4 quarts
   - ○ d) 24 cups

11. 3 tons =
   - ○ a) 3,000 lbs.
   - ○ b) 8,000 lbs.
   - ○ c) 9,000 lbs.
   - ○ d) 6,000 lbs.

12. 24 ft. =
   - ○ a) 5 yd.
   - ○ b) 6 yd.
   - ○ c) 3 yd.
   - ○ d) 8 yd.

Unit 5

Measurement Practice (I)

Name_____ Date_____

Find the match for each Column A measurement in Column B. Then find the match for each Column C measurement in Column D. Write the answers on the lines.

Column A	Column B	Column C	Column D
1. __ 16 oz.	a. 4 cups	13. __ 3 gallons	m. 3 yd.
2. __ 4 quarts	b. 1 yd.	14. __ 48 in.	n. 64 oz.
3. __ 6 ft.	c. 1 T.	15. __ 32 oz.	o. 40 quarts
4. __ 64 liquid oz.	d. 1 cup	16. __ 108 in.	p. 1 quart
5. __ 5 lbs.	e. 12 ft.	17. __ 3 T.	q. 10 ft.
6. __ 4 yd.	f. 2 yd.	18. __ 4 lbs.	r. 4 ft.
7. __ 2,000 lbs.	g. 1 gallon	19. __ 20 cups	s. 12 quarts
8. __ 24 in.	h. 1 lb.	20. __ 16 pints	t. 15 yd.
9. __ 2 pints	i. 2 quarts	21. __ 120 inches	u. 10 pints
10. __ 8 quarts	j. 80 oz.	22. __ 10 gallons	v. 6,000 lbs.
11. __ 36 inches	k. 2 ft.	23. __ 45 ft.	w. 2 lbs.
12. __ 8 liquid oz.	l. 2 gallons	24. __ 32 oz.	x. 2 gallons

Metric Units of Length

Name_____ Date_____

_____ **8 cm.**

_____ **2 cm.**

____ **1 cm.**

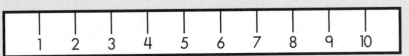

Use a ruler to measure the length of each line

1. _____   _____ cm.

2. _____   _____ cm.

3. _____   _____ cm.

4. _____   _____ cm.

Use a ruler to draw a line for each measurement.

5. 1 cm.   6. 4 cm.

7. 7 cm.

8. 8 cm.

9. 11 cm.

10. 14 cm.

11. Use an inch rule to draw a two-inch line.
    Measure the line with a metric ruler.

    2 in. = about _____ cm.

Metric Units of Length

| 100 centimeters or 100 cm. = 1 meter or 1 m. | 1,000 m. = 1 kilometer or 1 km. |

Find the length of each item to the nearest meter to complete the sentence.

1. I am about _____ m. tall.

2. The door closest to me is about _____ m. tall.

3. The wall closest to me is about _____ m. wide.

Find the equivalent measurement.

4. 100 cm. = _____ m.

5. 1,000 m. = _____ km.

6. 500 cm. = _____ km.

7. 7,000 m. = _____ km.

8. 1,000 cm. = _____ m.

9. 10,000 m. = _____ km.

10. 100,000 m. = _____ km.

11. 20 km. = _____ m.

12. 40 km. = _____ m.

13. 65 km. = _____ m.

Use a ruler that shows the equivalent metric and U.S. Customary units of length for each of the following.

14. 4 in. = about _____ cm.

15. 8 cm. = about _____ in.

16. 6 in. = about _____ cm.

17. 23 cm. = about _____ in.

18. 1 ft. = about _____ cm.

19. 28 cm. = about _____ in.

20. Use the answer you found for #18 to figure out the following.

   1 yd. = about _____ cm. or close to _____ m.

Metric Units Of Weight (Mass)

Name_____ Date_____

1,000 grams or 1,000 g. = 1 kilogram or 1 kg.

a feather = about 1 g.　　1 g. < 1 oz.　　a brick = about 1 kg.　　1 kg. > 1 lb.

Circle the correct unit of measurement used to measure the weight of each item.

1. **penny**　　　　g.　kg.　　　　2. **tree**　　　g.　kg.

3. **truck**　　　　g.　kg.　　　　4. **flower**　　g.　kg.

5. **bag of apples**　g.　kg.　　　　6. **sock**　　　g.　kg.

7. **rooster**　　　g.　kg.　　　　8. **chair**　　　g.　kg.

9. **pen**　　　　　g.　kg.　　　　10. **comb**　　g.　kg.

Find the equivalent measurement.

11. 1,000 g. = _____ kg.　　　　12. 10,000 g. = _____ kg.

13. 5,000 g. = _____ kg.　　　　14. 25,000 g. = _____ kg.

Write the answer.

15. Which weighs more, an ounce of sugar or a gram of sugar? _____

16. Which weighs more, a pound of salt or a kilogram of salt? _____

17. Which weighs more, one ton or 2,000 kilograms? _____

Metric Units of Volume

Name_____ Date_____

| 1 milliliter or 1 ml. = about 20 drops of liquid |
| 30 ml. = about 1 liquid oz. |

| 1 liter = 1000 ml. |
| 1 liter = a little more that 4 cups |
| 1 liter = a little more than 1 quart |

Circle the correct unit of measurement used to measure the capacity of each.

1. **teaspoon**   ml.   liter   2. **soup pot**   ml.   liter

3. **milk bottle**   ml.   liter   4. **ladle**   ml.   liter

5. **gas tank**   ml.   liter   6. **large jug**   ml.   liter

7. **eye dropper**   ml.   liter   8. **ketchup packet**   ml.   liter

Find the equivalent measurement.

9. 1,000 ml. = _____ liter

10. 5,000 ml. = _____ liters

11. 10,000 ml. = _____ liters

12. 4 liters = _____ ml.

13. 12 liters = _____ ml.

14. 2 liquid oz. = about _____ ml.

15. 1 cup (8 oz.) = about _____ ml.

16. 2 pints = almost _____ liter

17. 2 quarts = almost _____ liters

18. 1 gallon = almost _____ liters

Write the answer.

19. The store offers liter bottles of pop for 69¢ and
   quart bottles for 69¢. Which is a better value?   _____

20. A 2-quart container of milk and a 4-liter container
   of milk both cost $2.29. Which is a better value?   _____

Measurement Review (II)

Name_____ Date_____

Fill in the circle next to the correct answer.

1. A centimeter measures _____.

   ○ a) time   ○ c) volume

   ○ b) length   ○ d) weight

2. A milliliter measures _____.

   ○ a) time   ○ c) volume

   ○ b) length   ○ d) weight

3. A lemon can be weighed in _____.

   ○ a) liters   ○ c) grams

   ○ b) meters   ○ d) centimeters

4. A kilogram measures _____.

   ○ a) volume   ○ c) time

   ○ b) length   ○ d) weight

5. Which weighs the most?

   ○ a) 1,500 g.   ○ c) 1 kg.

   ○ b) 3,500 g.   ○ d) 3 kg.

6. How many cm. in 1 meter?

   ○ a) 1,000   ○ c) 100

   ○ b) 10   ○ d) 100,000

7. How many ml. in a liter?

   ○ a) 1,000   ○ c) 100

   ○ b) 10   ○ d) 100,000

8. 10 liters =

   ○ a) 10,000 ml.   ○ c) 1,000 ml.

   ○ b) 100 ml.   ○ d) 100,000 ml.

9. 20 km. =

   ○ a) 2,000 m.   ○ c) 200,000 m.

   ○ b) 20,000 m.   ○ d) 2,000,000 m.

10. Which weighs the least?

   ○ a) 200 g.   ○ c) 2 kg.

   ○ b) 2,000 g.   ○ d) 20 kg.

11. Which comparison is true?

   ○ a) 1 kg. < 1 g.   ○ c) 1 liter < 1 ml.

   ○ b) 1 cm. > 1 in.   ○ d) 1 meter > 1 cm.

12. 9,000 cm. =

   ○ a) 9 km.   ○ c) 90 m.

   ○ b) 9 m.   ○ d) 90 km.

Unit 5

Name_____ Date_____

Solve each problem.

1. Amanda is 4 ft. tall. What is her height in inches? _____

2. Kyle flew his kite 20 m. high. How high is that in centimeters? _____

3. Which weighs more, 3 T. or 3,000 kg.? _____

4. How many cups are in 3 quarts? _____

5. About many ounces equal 90 milliliters? _____

6. How many feet are in 27 yards? _____

7. What is the correct metric unit to measure the liquid volume of a spoon? _____

8. About how many centimeters equal 9 inches? _____

9. Which weighs more, 4 oz. or 4 g.? _____

10. How many pints are in 6 gallons? _____

11. How many ounces are in 5 pounds? _____

12. Which is heavier, a kilogram of tea or a pound of tea? _____

13. Draw a line $3\frac{3}{4}$ in. long.

14. Draw a line 11 cm. long.

Time: Calendars (1)

Name_____ Date_____

February						
S	M	T	W	T	F	S
	1	2	3	4	5	6
7	8	9	10	11	12	13
14	15	16	17	18	19	20
21	22	23	24	25	26	27
28						

March						
S	M	T	W	T	F	S
	1	2	3	4	5	6
7	8	9	10	11	12	13
14	15	16	17	18	19	20
21	22	23	24	25	26	27
28	29	30	31			

April						
S	M	T	W	T	F	S
				1	2	3
4	5	6	7	8	9	10
11	12	13	14	15	16	17
18	19	20	21	22	23	24
25	26	27	28	29	30	

Use the three-month calendar to answer each question.

1. How many days are in each month shown? _____ _____ _____

    February   March   April

2. Which day of the week is February 1? _____

3. Which day of the week is March 19? _____

4. Which day of the week is April 20? _____

5. How many Mondays are in March? _____

6. How many Saturdays are in April? _____

7. What date falls 2 weeks before March 29? _____

8. What date is the first Saturday in April? _____

Write the answers.

9. How many days are in 1 week? _____

10. How many days are in 2 weeks? _____

11. How many days are in 6 weeks? _____

12. How many days are in 12 weeks? _____

Unit 5

Time: Calendars (II)

Name_____ Date_____

January – 31 days	May – 31 days	September – 30 days
February – 28 days	June – 30 days	October – 31 days
March – 31 days	July – 31 days	November – 30 days
April – 30 days	August – 31 days	December – 31 days

There are usually 365 days in a year. A **leap year** falls every 4 years and has 366 days. In a leap year, February has 29 days.

Write the answers.

1. How many months have 31 days? _____   Multiply 31 by your answer.
$$\begin{array}{r} 31 \\ \times \boxed{} \\ \hline \boxed{} \end{array}$$

2. How many months have 30 days? _____   Multiply 30 by your answer.
$$\begin{array}{r} 30 \\ \times \boxed{} \\ \hline \boxed{} \end{array}$$

3. Add the two products

Add 28 to your sum. $\boxed{}$
(days in February) $+\ 28$
A year typically has $\boxed{}$ days.

4. How often does a leap year fall? _____

5. What date is added in a leap year? _____

6. Complete the pattern of leap years.   2000, 2004, _____, _____, 2016

Write T if the statement is true or F if it is false.

7. January has 30 days. _____   8. February usually has 29 days. _____

9. April has 31 days. _____   10. September has 30 days. _____

11. December has 31 days. _____   12. June has 31 days. _____

Time: Hours and Minutes

Name_____ Date_____

- There are 60 minutes in 1 hour.
- Each tick mark on a clock measures one minute of time.
- The numerals are 5 minutes apart.

 **4:52**

Write the number of minutes.

1. 2 hours _____   5 hours _____   7 hours _____

2. $8\frac{1}{2}$ hours _____ $9\frac{1}{2}$ hours _____   10 hours _____

Write the time.

3.

2:15 _____   _____   _____   _____

4.  _____   _____   _____   _____

5.  _____    _____    _____    _____

Unit 5

Time of Day

Name_____ Date_____

a.m. = before noon	12 a.m. hours
p.m. = after noon	+ 12 p.m. hours
	24 hours in one day

Write the number of hours.

1. 2 days _____   5 days _____   1 week _____

_____

Write the time before noon.

2.

3:30 a.m.   _____   _____   _____

_____

Write the time after noon.

3.

_____   _____   _____   _____

_____

Write the time you usually do each event listed. Include **a.m.** or **p.m.**

4. eat breakfast _____   do homework _____   go to bed at night _____

5. eat lunch _____   watch favorite T.V. show _____   wake up _____

Name_____ Date_____

How much time has **elapsed**, or passed, from 1:15 p.m. to 5:28 p.m.?

1:15 to 2:00 = 45 minutes   45
2:00 to 5:00 = 3 hours or 180 minutes   180
5:00 to 5:28 = 28 minutes   + 28
                                                    253 → 253 minutes = 6 hours, 13 minutes

Find the elapsed time. If the sum is more than 60 minutes, write the time two ways.

1. 7:10 a.m. to 8:15 a.m.

50
+15
65 minutes
or 1 hour, 5 minutes

2. 9:10 p.m. to 11:01 p.m.

3. 2:40 p.m. to 4:18 p.m.

4. 12:05 a.m. to 1:52 a.m.

5. 6:56 a.m. to 9:44 a.m.

6. 8:36 p.m. to 11:24 p.m.

7. 11:11 a.m. to 12:57 p.m.

8. 5:24 a.m. to 8:19 a.m.

9. 4:08 a.m. to 7:49 a.m.

10. 10:17 p.m. to 1:56 a.m.

Unit 5

Name_____ Date_____

June						
S	M	T	W	T	F	S
				1	2	3
4	5	6	7	8	9	10
11	12	13	14	15	16	17
18	19	20	21	22	23	24
25	26	27	28	29	30	

1. Which day of the week is June 8? _____

2. Which day of the week is June 27? _____

3. How many Fridays are in June? _____

4. What date is the second Wednesday of June? _____ The 4th Monday? _____

5. What date falls 12 days before June 25? _____ 17 days before June 25? _____

6. List the three other months that have only 30 days.

_____

7. How many days does a year usually have? _____ A leap year? _____

8. How many days are in 3 weeks? _____ In 7 weeks? _____ In 9 weeks? _____

9. How many hours are in 1 day? _____ In 4 days? _____ In 6 days? _____

10. How is 8 o'clock before noon written? _____ 8 o'clock after noon? _____

11. What time is shown? _____

12. What will the next whole hour be? _____

13. How many minutes are there until the next whole hour? _____

14. How much time will have elapsed from what is shown now until 3:19? _____

Name_____ Date_____

Fill in the circle next to the correct answer.

1. Which month has 30 days?

    ○ a) August   ○ c) September
    ○ b) December   ○ d) October

2. Which month has 31 days?

    ○ a) April   ○ c) June
    ○ b) May   ○ d) November

3. Identify the leap year.

    ○ a) 2005   ○ c) 2006
    ○ b) 2010   ○ d) 2012

4. How many days are in 8 weeks?

    ○ a) 48   ○ c) 54
    ○ b) 63   ○ d) 56

5. How many hours are in 6 days?

    ○ a) 124   ○ c) 120
    ○ b) 142   ○ d) 144

6. How many minutes are in 3 hours?

    ○ a) 180   ○ c) 240
    ○ b) 360   ○ d) 120

Clock A   **Clock B**
(a.m. time)   (a.m. time)

7. What time does Clock A show?

    ○ a) 5:42   ○ c) 6:42
    ○ b) 7:42   ○ d) 7:38

8. What time does Clock B show?

    ○ a) 8:14   ○ c) 8:16
    ○ b) 8:24   ○ d) 8:44

9. What time would Clock A show after 15 more minutes?

    ○ a) 6:59   ○ c) 7:02
    ○ b) 7:07   ○ d) 6:57

10. What time would Clock B show after 37 more minutes?

    ○ a) 8:51   ○ c) 8:41
    ○ b) 8:39   ○ d) 8:32

11. What is the elapsed time between Clock A and Clock B?

    ○ a) 1 hour, 23 min.   ○ c) 1 hour, 8 min.
    ○ b) 1 hour, 22 min.   ○ d) 1 hour, 32 min.

Unit 5

Measurement Practice (III)

Name_____ Date_____

Draw a line to show the length.

1. $1\frac{1}{2}$ in.

2. 6 cm.

3. $3\frac{3}{4}$ in.

4. 10 cm.

Find the equivalent measurement.

5. 24 in. = _____ ft.

6. 2 days = _____ hours

7. 36 in. = _____ yd.

8. 1 year = _____ days

9. 4 cups = _____ pints

10. 25 km. = _____ m.

11. 12 quarts = _____ gallons

12. 2 kg. = _____ g.

13. 200 cm. = _____ m.

14. 64 oz. = _____ lbs.

15. 3,000 m. = _____ km.

16. 300 minutes = _____ hours

17. 10,000 g. = _____ kg.

18. 9 weeks = _____ days

19. 6,000 lbs. = _____ T.

20. 8 days = _____ hours

Write the number of days in each month for a typical year (not a leap year).

21. January_____   February_____   March_____   April_____

22. May_____   June_____   July_____   August_____

23. September_____   October_____   November_____   December_____

Measurement Review (III)

Name_____ Date_____

Fill in the circle next to the correct answer.

1. _____

   The line above measures _____.

   ○ a) 1 in.   ○ c) 3 cm.

   ○ b) 4 cm.   ○ d) $1\frac{1}{2}$ in.

2. 1 lb. of feathers weighs _____.

   ○ a) 10 oz.   ○ c) 16 g.
   ○ b) 16 oz.   ○ d) 10 g.

3. 14 pints equal _____.

   ○ a) 7 quarts   ○ c) 7 gallons
   ○ b) 26 cups   ○ d) 6 quarts

4. 1 liquid oz. equals about _____.

   ○ a) 3 ml.   ○ c) 30 ml
   ○ b) 60 ml.   ○ d) 1 liter

5. A liter equals a little more than _____.

   ○ a) 1 cup   ○ c) 4 pints
   ○ b) 2 cups   ○ d) 1 quart

6. 5 T. equals _____.

   ○ a) 1,000 lbs.   ○ c) 4,000 kg.
   ○ b) 10,000 lbs. ○ d) 10,000 kg.

7. How many days are in May and June together?

   ○ a) 60   ○ c) 62
   ○ b) 59   ○ d) 61

8. How many days are in two non-leap years?

   ○ a) 730   ○ c) 731
   ○ b) 732   ○ d) 728

9. How many minutes are in 8 hours?

   ○ a) 540   ○ c) 560
   ○ b) 480   ○ d) 420

10. How many hours are in 1 week?

    ○ a) 120   ○ c) 144
    ○ b) 168   ○ d) 192

11. How many minutes are in 12 hours?

    ○ a) 720   ○ c) 600
    ○ b) 240   ○ d) 480

12. What is the elapsed time between 1:30 p.m. and 3:48 p.m.?

    ○ a) 2 hours, 28 min.   ○ c) 2 hours, 18 min.
    ○ b) 3 hours, 18 min.   ○ d) 3 hours, 28 min.

Unit 5

Roman Numerals

Name_____ Date_____

We use the decimal number system whose numerals are 1, 2, 3, 4, 5, 6, 7, 8, 9, and 0. The Roman numeral system uses letters as numerals.

I = 1	**V** = 5	**X** = 10
II = I + I = 2	**VIII** = V + I + I + I = 8	**XV** = X + V = 15
IV = V – I = 4	**IX** = X – I = 9	**XX** = X + X = 20

Write the number using decimal system numerals.

1. III = ____   V = ____   VII = ____   X = ____

2. IV = ____   IX = ____   XX = ____   XII = ____

3. XXX = ____   XXV = ____   XIV = ____   XVII = ____

4. XIX = ____   XXVI = ____   XXIV = ____   XXIX = ____

5. XXXIII = ____   XXXII = ____   XXXXIX = ____   XXXVIII = ____

Write the Roman numeral.

6. 2 = _____   4 = _____   5 = _____   9 = _____

7. 10 = _____   15 = _____   20 = _____   23 = _____

8. 16 = _____   19 = _____   27 = _____   30 = _____

9. 24 = _____   29 = _____   35 = _____   38 = _____

10. 40 = _____   44 = _____   39 = _____   46 = _____

Bar Graphs

Name_____ Date_____

A bar graph compares **data**, or information.

This bar graph shows the number of sit-ups completed by four students during gym class.

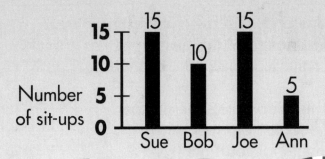

Number of sit-ups

Four scouting troops sold cases of boxed mixed nuts to raise money.

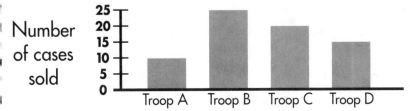

Number of cases sold

1. Which troop sold the most cases? _____ Which troop sold the least? _____

2. Which troop sold more cases, Troop C or Troop D? _____

3. Which troop sold fewer cases, Troop A or Troop C? _____

4. How many more cases were sold by Troop B than Troop D? _____

5. How many fewer cases were sold by Troop A than Troop B? _____

6. Draw a bar graph below to show the number of slices eaten by each of four contestants in a watermelon-eating contest.

- Lia ate 20 watermelon slices.
- Mary ate 5 fewer slices than Lia.
- Bill at 25 watermelon slices.
- Roy at 5 more slices than Bill.

Line Graphs

Line graphs show changes in data. The points on the graph are connected to plot the changes.

This graph plots the number of books Tom read each month for four months.

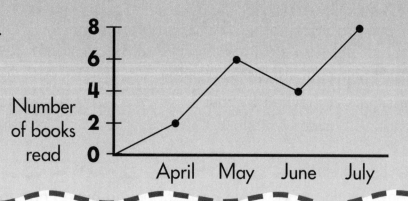

This graph plots the number of hours Amy spent watching T.V. each week.

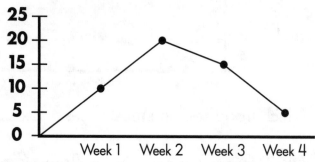

1. In which week did Amy watch the most T.V.? _____ The least? _____

2. How many more hours did Amy watch T.V. in Week 2 than in Week 4? _____

3. Did the number of hours increase or decrease between Weeks 1 and 2? _____

4. Did they increase or decrease between Weeks 3 and 4? _____

5. In which week do you think Amy had more homework than usual? _____

6. Draw and plot a line graph to show the number of raffle tickets sold by Mr. Scott's third grade class from Monday through Thursday.

- 50 tickets were sold on Monday.
- Twice as many were sold on Tuesday.
- 200 were sold on Wednesday.
- Half as many were sold on Thursday.

Geometry: Lines

Name_____ Date_____

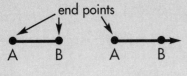 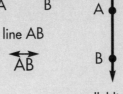 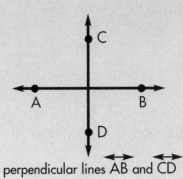

line segment AB

or $\overline{AB}$

A line segment has 2 end points.

ray AB

or $\overrightarrow{AB}$

A ray has 1 end point.

line AB

$\overleftrightarrow{AB}$

parallel lines AB and CD

or $\overleftrightarrow{AB}$ // $\overleftrightarrow{CD}$

perpendicular lines $\overleftrightarrow{AB}$ and $\overleftrightarrow{CD}$

or $\overleftrightarrow{AB} \perp \overleftrightarrow{CD}$

Identify each line.

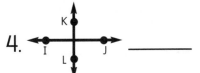

1. Q R _____ U V _____

2. M N _____ Y Z _____

3. E F G H _____

4. K I L J _____ S T _____

5. O P _____ W X _____

Draw.

6. $\overline{EF}$ $\overrightarrow{OP}$

7. $\overleftrightarrow{JK}$ // $\overleftrightarrow{LM}$

8. $\overleftrightarrow{UV}$ $\overleftrightarrow{GH} \perp \overleftrightarrow{IJ}$

Geometry: Angles

Name_____ Date_____

angle ABC or ∠ABC

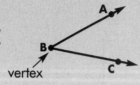

- A **vertex** is an endpoint shared by two rays.
- An angle is made up of two rays that share a common endoint.

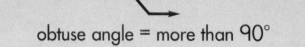

acute angle = less than 90°   obtuse angle = more than 90°   right angle = 90°

Name each angle, then underline the letter that stands for its vertex.

1.  ∠DEF

   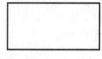 [   ]

2. 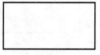 [   ]

   [   ]

Write **acute, obtuse,** or **right** to identify each angle.

3. _____ _____ _____

4. _____ _____ _____

5. _____ _____ _____

Complete each sentence.

6. An angle measuring less than 90° is called an _____ angle.

7. An angle measuring exactly 90° is called a _____ angle.

8. An angle measuring more than 90° is called an _____ angle.

Geometry: Triangles

Name_____ Date_____

A **triangle** is a polygon with three sides and three vertexes.

Equilateral triangles have
3 sides of equal length.

Isosceles triangles have
2 sides of equal length.

Scalene triangles have
no sides of equal length.

Write **equilateral**, **isosceles**, or **scalene** to identify each triangle.

1. _____ _____ _____

2. _____ _____ _____

3. _____ _____ _____

4. _____ _____ _____

5. _____ _____ _____

Complete each sentence.

6. A triangle with no sides of equal length is a _____ triangle.

7. A triangle with two sides of equal length is an _____ triangle.

8. A triangle with three sides of equal length is an _____ triangle.

Geometry: Polygons

Name_____ Date_____

A **polygon** may be named by the number of its sides.

Name	Sides	Name	Sides
triangle	3	heptagon	7
quadrilateral	4	octagon	8
pentagon	5	nonagon	9
hexagon	6	decagon	10

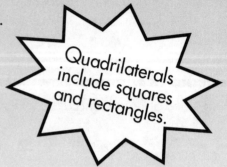

Quadrilaterals include squares and rectangles.

Write the answer.

1. What is the name of an eight-sided polygon?_____

2. What is the name of a three-sided polygon?_____

3. How many sides does a pentagon have?_____

4. How many sides does a decagon have?_____

5. What is the name of a four-sided polygon?_____

Write the name of each polygon.

  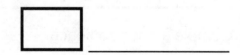

6._____ _____ _____

 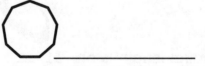 

7._____ _____ _____

  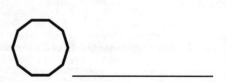

8._____ _____ _____

Name_____ Date_____

If this figure could be "folded" along its **lines of symmetry,** the size and shape of the opposite sides of the figure would match exactly.

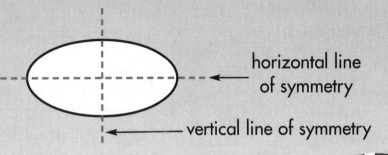

horizontal line of symmetry ←

← vertical line of symmetry

Circle the one in each row that has lines of symmetry.

1.

2. 4   0   7   5

3. R   Q   I   L

4. Name three polygons that can have lines of symmetry.

_____   _____   _____

Unit 5

Congruent figures have exactly the same size and shape.

Circle the two congruent shapes.

5. a)   b)   c)   d)

6. a)   b)   c)   d)

7. a)   b)   c)   d)

8. If a figure has a line of symmetry, are its opposite sides congruent? **yes   no**

Geometry: Perimeter

Name_____ Date_____

The **perimeter** of a polygon
is the distance around it.

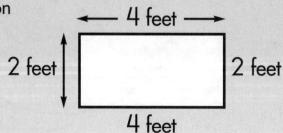

Find the perimeter of each figure.

1.

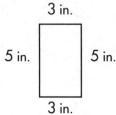

perimeter = _____

2.

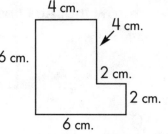

perimeter = _____

3.

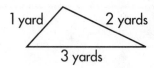

perimeter = _____

4.

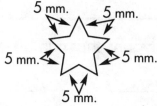

perimeter = _____

5. Sam's garden is a perfect square. Each side measures 8 feet.
What is the perimeter of his garden?   _____

6. Leslie drew a triangle on the board. Each side measured
30 centimeters. What is the perimeter of the triangle? _____

7. What is the perimeter of a hexagon whose sides all equal
4 yards?   _____

8. If two sides of a rectangular field are 2 km. wide, and two
sides are 4 km. long, what is the perimeter of the field? _____

9. What is the perimeter of a decagon whose sides all equal
8 yards?   _____

Geometry Review (I)

Name_____ Date_____

Fill in the circle next to the correct answer.

1. $\overrightarrow{CD}$ means _____.
   - ○ a) ray CD
   - ○ b) line CD
   - ○ c) line segment CD
   - ○ d) angle CD

2. Lines that are the same distance apart but never touch are called _____.
   - ○ a) perpendicular
   - ○ b) line segments
   - ○ c) parallel
   - ○ d) angles

3. How many endpoints does a ray have?
   - ○ a) 0
   - ○ b) 1
   - ○ c) 2
   - ○ d) 3

4. ◄─┼─► These lines are _____.
   - ○ a) parallel
   - ○ b) acute
   - ○ c) perpendicular
   - ○ d) obtuse

5. An endpoint shared by two rays is a(n) _____.
   - ○ a) angle
   - ○ b) vertex
   - ○ c) acute
   - ○ d) polygon

6. Which of these is not a polygon?
   - ○ a) triangle
   - ○ b) circle
   - ○ c) rectangle
   - ○ d) square

7. A nonagon has _____ sides.
   - ○ a) 9
   - ○ b) 7
   - ○ c) 10
   - ○ d) 8

8. A quadrilateral has _____ sides.
   - ○ a) 6
   - ○ b) 4
   - ○ c) 3
   - ○ d) 7

9. A heptagon has _____ sides.
   - ○ a) 5
   - ○ b) 9
   - ○ c) 7
   - ○ d) 10

10. Which polygon has six sides?
    - ○ a) heptagon
    - ○ b) pentagon
    - ○ c) octogon
    - ○ d) hexagon

11. A triangle with 3 equal sides is _____.
    - ○ a) obtuse
    - ○ b) acute
    - ○ c) equilateral
    - ○ d) parallel

12. A scalene triangle has _____ equal sides.
    - ○ a) 3
    - ○ b) 0
    - ○ c) 2
    - ○ d) 1

Unit 5

Geometry Review (II)

Name_____ Date_____

Fill in the circle next to the correct answer.

1. ∠RST means _____.

   ○ a) triangle RST   ○ c) line RST
   ○ b) angle RST   ○ d) ray RST

2. The symbol ⊥ means _____.

   ○ a) symmetrical to   ○ c) parallel to
   ○ b) congruent to   ○ d) perpendicular to

3. An obtuse angle is _____ 90°.

   ○ a) more than   ○ c) less than
   ○ b) equal to   ○ d) close to

4. A right angle is _____ 90°.

   ○ a) more than   ○ c) less than
   ○ b) equal to   ○ d) close to

5. Which letter has a line of symmetry?

   ○ a) J   ○ c) H
   ○ b) Q   ○ d) F

6. Congruent means having the same _____.

   ○ a) size and angle   ○ c) shape
   ○ b) size and shape   ○ d) angle and shape

7. A square whose sides each equal 3 cm. has a perimeter of _____.

   ○ a) 9 cm.   ○ c) 12 cm.
   ○ b) 12 m.   ○ d) 6 cm.

8. The perimeter of a pentagon whose sides all equal 7 ft. is _____.

   ○ a) 42 ft.   ○ c) 35 ft.
   ○ b) 25 ft.   ○ d) 49 ft.

9. The perimeter of a triangle whose sides all measure 8 m. is _____.

   ○ a) 24 m.   ○ c) 16 m.
   ○ b) 32 m.   ○ d) 24 cm.

10. How many polygons are in a group of 3 triangles, 2 squares, 5 circles, and 4 nonagons?

   ○ a) 14   ○ c) 10
   ○ b) 9   ○ d) 12

11. The perimeter of a decagon whose sides all equal 12 cm. is _____.

   ○ a) 118 cm.   ○ c) 120 cm.
   ○ b) 144 cm.   ○ d) 96 cm.

Name_____ Date_____

Fill in the circle next to the correct answer.

1. 4 + 9 =

   ○ a) 14   ○ c) 15
   ○ b) 13   ○ d) 12

2. 16 – 7 =

   ○ a) 8   ○ c) 9
   ○ b) 6   ○ d) 7

3. 8 + 7 =

   ○ a) 14   ○ c) 13
   ○ b) 15   ○ d) 16

4. 13 – 5 =

   ○ a) 8   ○ c) 9
   ○ b) 7   ○ d) 6

5. 21 + 6 =

   ○ a) 25   ○ c) 28
   ○ b) 29   ○ d) 27

6. 39 – 5 =

   ○ a) 34   ○ c) 35
   ○ b) 33   ○ d) 32

7. 35 + 9 =

   ○ a) 43   ○ c) 44
   ○ b) 46   ○ d) 42

8. 24 – 7 =

   ○ a) 18   ○ c) 16
   ○ b) 17   ○ d) 15

9. 23 + 46 =

   ○ a) 69   ○ c) 68
   ○ b) 71   ○ d) 70

10. 68 – 51 =

   ○ a) 27   ○ c) 17
   ○ b) 16   ○ d) 26

11. 18 + 75 =

   ○ a) 95   ○ c) 93
   ○ b) 94   ○ d) 92

12. 91 – 36 =

   ○ a) 65   ○ c) 54
   ○ b) 55   ○ d) 64

Unit 6

Name_____ Date_____

Fill in the circle next to the correct answer.

1. In the equation 6 + 9 = 15, _____.
   - ○ a) 15 is the addend
   - ○ b) 6 and 9 are addends
   - ○ c) 15 is the difference
   - ○ d) 9 and 6 are sums

2. In the equation 12 – 4 = 8, _____.
   - ○ a) 4 is the minuend
   - ○ b) 12 is the subtrahend
   - ○ c) 8 is the difference
   - ○ d) 8 is the minuend

3. 125 + 52 =
   - ○ a) 176
   - ○ b) 166
   - ○ c) 167
   - ○ d) 177

4. 297 – 36 =
   - ○ a) 261
   - ○ b) 162
   - ○ c) 161
   - ○ d) 151

5. 331 + 17 + 11 =
   - ○ a) 379
   - ○ b) 358
   - ○ c) 369
   - ○ d) 359

6. 458 – ____ = 234
   - ○ a) 234
   - ○ b) 224
   - ○ c) 232
   - ○ d) 222

7. 568 + 389 =
   - ○ a) 957
   - ○ b) 857
   - ○ c) 867
   - ○ d) 967

8. 632 – 476 =
   - ○ a) 166
   - ○ b) 156
   - ○ c) 165
   - ○ d) 155

9. 348 + ____ = 642
   - ○ a) 284
   - ○ b) 394
   - ○ c) 294
   - ○ d) 384

10. 800 – ____ = 373
    - ○ a) 429
    - ○ b) 425
    - ○ c) 437
    - ○ d) 427

11. 156 + ____ = 904
    - ○ a) 648
    - ○ b) 748
    - ○ c) 646
    - ○ d) 649

12. 909 – ____ = 373
    - ○ a) 536
    - ○ b) 556
    - ○ c) 546
    - ○ d) 526

Name_____ Date_____

Fill in the circle next to the correct answer.

1. The product of 4 x 9 and 6 x 6 is _____.

   ○ a) 27   ○ c) 32
   ○ b) 36   ○ d) 42

2. Any number multiplied by zero equals _____.

   ○ a) itself   ○ c) half of itself
   ○ b) zero   ○ d) one

3. 48 is a product of which two factors?

   ○ a) 6 and 7   ○ c) 6 and 8
   ○ b) 7 and 8   ○ d) 8 and 9

4. 72 is a product of which two factors?

   ○ a) 7 and 9   ○ c) 9 and 6
   ○ b) 8 and 7   ○ d) 8 and 9

5. 30 is not a product of which two factors?

   ○ a) 5 and 6   ○ c) 3 and 10
   ○ b) 4 and 8   ○ d) 15 and 2

6. 100 is not a product of which two factors?

   ○ a) 10 and 10   ○ c) 5 and 25
   ○ b) 5 and 20   ○ d) 4 and 25

7. 30 x 6 =

   ○ a) 240   ○ c) 108
   ○ b) 120   ○ d) 180

8. 70 x 9 =

   ○ a) 560   ○ c) 630
   ○ b) 640   ○ d) 540

9. 23 x 3 =

   ○ a) 69   ○ c) 72
   ○ b) 66   ○ d) 96

10. 64 x 2 =

   ○ a) 132   ○ c) 124
   ○ b) 138   ○ d) 128

11. 57 x 5 =

   ○ a) 275   ○ c) 295
   ○ b) 285   ○ d) 305

12. 28 x 9 =

   ○ a) 262   ○ c) 272
   ○ b) 252   ○ d) 242

Unit 6

Practice Test: Basic Functions (IV)

Name_____ Date_____

Fill in the circle next to the correct answer.

1. The number 2 in 6 ÷ 3 = 2 is the _____.

   ○ a) product   ○ c) quotient
   ○ b) divisor   ○ d) dividend

2. The number 6 in 6 ÷ 3 = 2 is the _____.

   ○ a) product   ○ c) quotient
   ○ b) divisor   ○ d) dividend

3. The number 3 in 6 ÷ 3 = 2 is the _____.

   ○ a) product   ○ c) quotient
   ○ b) divisor   ○ d) dividend

4. Zero divided by any number equals _____.

   ○ a) one   ○ c) zero
   ○ b) that number   ○ d) half of itself

5. 12 ÷ 3 =

   ○ a) 3   ○ c) 5
   ○ b) 4   ○ d) 6

6. 28 ÷ 4 =

   ○ a) 7   ○ c) 9
   ○ b) 6   ○ d) 8

7. 54 ÷ 9 =

   ○ a) 7   ○ c) 6
   ○ b) 9   ○ d) 5

8. 81 ÷ 9 =

   ○ a) 6   ○ c) 8
   ○ b) 9   ○ d) 7

9. 42 ÷ 6 =

   ○ a) 7   ○ c) 8
   ○ b) 6   ○ d) 9

10. 56 ÷ 7 =

   ○ a) 8   ○ c) 9
   ○ b) 7   ○ d) 4

11. 35 ÷ ___ = 5

   ○ a) 6   ○ c) 5
   ○ b) 8   ○ d) 7

12. ___ ÷ 7 = 7

   ○ a) 49   ○ c) 42
   ○ b) 48   ○ d) 35

Name_____ Date_____

Fill in the circle next to the correct answer.

1. 165 rounded to the nearest ten is _____.
   - ○ a) 166
   - ○ b) 160
   - ○ c) 200
   - ○ d) 170

2. 94,681 rounded to the nearest hundred is _____.
   - ○ a) 95,000
   - ○ b) 94,700
   - ○ c) 94,690
   - ○ d) 94,780

3. Rounded to the nearest ten, the estimated sum of 535 + 429 is _____.
   - ○ a) 970
   - ○ b) 990
   - ○ c) 980
   - ○ d) 960

4. Rounded to the nearest ten, the estimated difference of 964 – 212 is _____.
   - ○ a) 760
   - ○ b) 750
   - ○ c) 740
   - ○ d) 770

5. What fraction is shaded?
   - ○ a) $\frac{2}{9}$
   - ○ b) $\frac{2}{3}$
   - ○ c) $\frac{7}{9}$
   - ○ d) $\frac{6}{9}$

6. What fraction is shaded?
   - ○ a) $\frac{1}{10}$
   - ○ b) $\frac{9}{10}$
   - ○ c) $\frac{4}{5}$
   - ○ d) $\frac{8}{10}$

7. A numerator shows the number of parts _____.
   - ○ a) being counted
   - ○ b) in the whole
   - ○ c) added
   - ○ d) multiplied

8. A denominator shows the number of parts _____.
   - ○ a) being counted
   - ○ b) in the whole
   - ○ c) added
   - ○ d) multiplied

9. Five out of nine slices of pie are served with ice cream. What fraction is not?
   - ○ a) $\frac{5}{9}$
   - ○ b) $\frac{4}{5}$
   - ○ c) $\frac{4}{9}$
   - ○ d) $\frac{2}{3}$

10. Three of the bakery's eight cakes are chocolate. What fraction is not?
    - ○ a) $\frac{5}{8}$
    - ○ b) $\frac{3}{5}$
    - ○ c) $\frac{3}{8}$
    - ○ d) $\frac{1}{3}$

11. 5 is _____ of 15.
    - ○ a) $\frac{1}{3}$
    - ○ b) $\frac{1}{4}$
    - ○ c) $\frac{1}{5}$
    - ○ d) $\frac{1}{2}$

12. 6 is _____ of 42.
    - ○ a) $\frac{1}{6}$
    - ○ b) $\frac{1}{7}$
    - ○ c) $\frac{1}{8}$
    - ○ d) $\frac{1}{4}$

Unit 6

Name_____ Date_____

Fill in the circle next to the correct answer.

1. The value of 3 in 38 is _____.
   - ○ a) 300
   - ○ b) 3
   - ○ c) 30
   - ○ d) 3,000

2. The value of 7 in 789 is _____.
   - ○ a) 7
   - ○ b) 7,000
   - ○ c) 700
   - ○ d) 70

3. The value of 9 in 4,932 is _____.
   - ○ a) 90
   - ○ b) 9,000
   - ○ c) 900
   - ○ d) 9

4. The value of 0 in 20,846 is _____.
   - ○ a) 20,000
   - ○ b) 0
   - ○ c) 2,000
   - ○ d) 200

5. The value of 5 in 57,121 is _____.
   - ○ a) 5,000
   - ○ b) 500
   - ○ c) 50,000
   - ○ d) 50

6. In which place is the 4 in 14,389?
   - ○ a) ten thousands
   - ○ b) hundreds
   - ○ c) ones
   - ○ d) thousands

7. In which place is the 5 in 53,186?
   - ○ a) thousands
   - ○ b) ten thousands
   - ○ c) hundreds
   - ○ d) tens

8. If the 8 in 38,243 were changed to 5, the value would change to be _____.
   - ○ a) 30.000 less
   - ○ b) 300
   - ○ c) 3,000
   - ○ d) 3.000 less

9. The Roman numeral V represents _____.
   - ○ a) 10
   - ○ b) 5
   - ○ c) 1
   - ○ d) 4

10. XXIII represents _____.
    - ○ a) 13
    - ○ b) 28
    - ○ c) 22
    - ○ d) 23

11. XXXIX represents _____.
    - ○ a) 39
    - ○ b) 34
    - ○ c) 38
    - ○ d) 36

12. The Roman numeral for 47 is _____.
    - ○ a) XXXVII
    - ○ b) XXXXIX
    - ○ c) XXXXVI
    - ○ d) XXXXVII

Practice Test: Numbers (II)

Name_____ Date_____

Fill in the circle next to the correct answer.

1. 432 > ___

○ a) 423   ○ c) 434
○ b) 432   ○ d) 433

2. 6,733 < ___

○ a) 6,725   ○ c) 6,713
○ b) 6,733   ○ d) 6,773

3. 418 < 748 < ___ < 847 < 871

○ a) 744   ○ c) 874
○ b) 487   ○ d) 784

4. 1,717 > ___ > 1,711

○ a) 1,731   ○ c) 1,773
○ b) 1,713   ○ d) 1,711

5. 24,242 < ___ < 24,422

○ a) 24,244   ○ c) 24,424
○ b) 24,422   ○ d) 24,444

6. Which pattern shows the rule **add 7**?

○ a) 7, 14, 28, 56   ○ c) 3, 11, 19, 27
○ b) 7, 14, 21, 28   ○ d) 28, 21, 14, 7

7. Which pattern shows the rule **subtract 8**?

○ a) 64, 57, 50, 43   ○ c) 8, 16, 32, 64
○ b) 32, 25, 18, 11   ○ d) 24, 16, 8, 0

8. The rule for the pattern **6, 12, 24, 48** is ___.

○ a) add 12   ○ c) divide by 2
○ b) multiply by 2   ○ d) add 6

9. The rule for the pattern **72, 60, 48, 36** is ___.

○ a) divide by 12   ○ c) subtract 14
○ b) subtract 6   ○ d) subtract 12

10. **0, 15, 30, 45, 60, 75, ___**

○ a) 85   ○ c) 90
○ b) 95   ○ d) 105

11. **108, 96, 84, 72, 60, 48, ___**

○ a) 34   ○ c) 38
○ b) 36   ○ d) 32

12. **1, 5, 9, 13, 17, 21, ___**

○ a) 24   ○ c) 23
○ b) 26   ○ d) 25

Unit 6

Practice Test: Money

Fill in the circle next to the correct answer.

1. Four dollars, twenty-three cents written in decimal form is _____.
   - a) $4.32
   - b) 4.23¢
   - c) $4.023
   - d) $4.23

2. Sixty dollars, two cents written in decimal form is _____.
   - a) $60.20
   - b) $60.2
   - c) $60.02
   - d) $60.2¢

3. Three-tenths plus four hundredths of a dollar is _____.
   - a) $0.34
   - b) $3.40
   - c) $0.34
   - d) $34.00

4. $\frac{8}{10}$ of one dollar is _____.
   - a) $0.08
   - b) 8¢
   - c) 80¢
   - d) $8.10

5. $1.00 + 78¢ =
   - a) .178¢
   - b) $17.8
   - c) $1.078
   - d) $1.78

6. $3.42 – 35¢ =
   - a) $3.07
   - b) $3.17
   - c) $3.05
   - d) $3.005

7. $8.84 + $3.64 =
   - a) $11.48
   - b) $12.38
   - c) $12.48
   - d) $11.38

8. $7.24 – $4.68 =
   - a) $3.56
   - b) $2.66
   - c) $3.66
   - d) $2.56

9. $5.25 + $3.69 =
   - a) $9.04
   - b) $8.94
   - c) $9.94
   - d) $8.84

10. $6.00 – $2.39 =
    - a) $3.61
    - b) $4.71
    - c) $3.71
    - d) $4.61

11. $5.99 + 7.98 =
    - a) $12.97
    - b) $13.97
    - c) $13.98
    - d) $13.87

12. $9.17 – $3.78 =
    - a) $6.39
    - b) $5.29
    - c) $5.39
    - d) $6.29

Practice Test: Measurement

Name_____ Date_____

Fill in the circle next to the correct answer.

1. 4 yd. =
   - ○ a) 8 ft.
   - ○ b) 12 ft.
   - ○ c) 128 in.
   - ○ d) 16 ft.

2. 5 lbs. =
   - ○ a) 96 oz.
   - ○ b) 60 oz.
   - ○ c) 72 oz.
   - ○ d) 80 oz.

3. 1 gallon equals _____.
   - ○ a) 2 quarts
   - ○ b) 4 pints
   - ○ c) 8 cups
   - ○ d) 128 liquid oz.

4. 3 liters >
   - ○ a) 30,000 ml.
   - ○ b) 3 quarts
   - ○ c) 6 quarts
   - ○ d) 12 pints

5. 10,000 g. =
   - ○ a) 1 kg.
   - ○ b) 10 kg.
   - ○ c) 100 kg.
   - ○ d) 1,000 kg.

6. Which length is longest?
   - ○ a) 2 km.
   - ○ b) 20,000 cm.
   - ○ c) 2,000 m.
   - ○ d) 20 km.

7. 12 weeks =
   - ○ a) 84 days
   - ○ b) 76 days
   - ○ c) 74 days
   - ○ d) 82 days

8. Which month has 30 days?
   - ○ a) August
   - ○ b) July
   - ○ c) June
   - ○ d) May

9. 3 weeks from March 4 would be _____.
   - ○ a) March 25
   - ○ b) March 26
   - ○ c) March 24
   - ○ d) March 23

10. 8 hours =
    - ○ a) 420 min.
    - ○ b) 560 min.
    - ○ c) 420 min.
    - ○ d) 480 min.

11. The elapsed time between 1:30 p.m. and 2:48 p.m. is _____.
    - ○ a) 2 hours, 18 min.
    - ○ b) 1 hours, 18 min.
    - ○ c) 1 hours, 28 min.
    - ○ d) 1 hours, 48 min.

12. The elapsed time between 8:14 a.m. and 12:12 p.m. is _____.
    - ○ a) 4 hours, 56 min.
    - ○ b) 3 hours, 58 min.
    - ○ c) 3 hours, 54 min.
    - ○ d) 4 hours, 58 min.

Unit 6

Practice Test: Graphs

Name_____ Date_____

Fill in the circle next to the correct answer.

1. A bar graph ____ data.
   - ○ a) compares
   - ○ b) numbers
   - ○ c) shows changes in
   - ○ d) alphabetizes

2. A line graph ____ data.
   - ○ a) compares
   - ○ b) numbers
   - ○ c) shows changes in
   - ○ d) alphabetizes

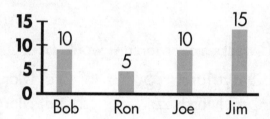

Number of sweets eaten in one week

3. Which boys ate the same number of sweets?
   - ○ a) Bob and Ron
   - ○ b) Jim and Ron
   - ○ c) Joe and Ron
   - ○ d) Bob and Joe

4. Who ate 3 times as many sweets as Ron?
   - ○ a) no one
   - ○ b) Joe
   - ○ c) Bob
   - ○ d) Jim

5. How many sweets did the boys eat altogether?
   - ○ a) 35
   - ○ b) 60
   - ○ c) 40
   - ○ d) 45

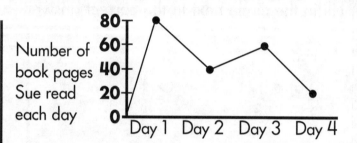

Number of book pages Sue read each day

6. On which day did Sue read the least?
   - ○ a) Day 1
   - ○ b) Day 3
   - ○ c) Day 2
   - ○ d) Day 4

7. On which day did she read 16 x 5 pages?
   - ○ a) Day 1
   - ○ b) Day 2
   - ○ c) Day 3
   - ○ d) Day 4

8. On which day did she read half as much as she did on Day 3?
   - ○ a) Day 1
   - ○ b) Day 2
   - ○ c) Day 4
   - ○ d) no day

9. On which day did she read $\frac{1}{4}$ as much as she did on Day 1?
   - ○ a) Day 2
   - ○ b) Day 3
   - ○ c) Day 4
   - ○ d) no day

10. On which day did the number of pages she read equal $\frac{4}{10}$ of 100?
   - ○ a) Day 1
   - ○ b) Day 2
   - ○ c) Day 3
   - ○ d) Day 4

Name_____ Date_____

Fill in the circle next to the correct answer.

1. A•————————•B is a(n) _____.
   - ○ a) line
   - ○ b) ray
   - ○ c) angle
   - ○ d) line segment

2. F•————————➤G is a(n) _____.
   - ○ a) line
   - ○ b) angle
   - ○ c) line segment
   - ○ d) ray

3. ◄——•——•——➤ is a(n) _____.
   W   X
   - ○ a) angle
   - ○ b) line
   - ○ c) ray
   - ○ d) line segment

4. $\overleftrightarrow{RS}$ // $\overleftrightarrow{TV}$ means lines RS and TV are _____.
   - ○ a) parallel
   - ○ b) congruent
   - ○ c) perpendicular
   - ○ d) equilateral

5. $\overleftrightarrow{LM}$ ⊥ $\overleftrightarrow{NO}$ means lines LM and NO are _____.
   - ○ a) congruent
   - ○ b) parallel
   - ○ c) equilateral
   - ○ d) perpendicular

6. A(n) _____ has only one endpoint.
   - ○ a) line
   - ○ b) angle
   - ○ c) ray
   - ○ d) line segment

7. An acute angle measures _____.
   - ○ a) more than 90°
   - ○ b) 180°
   - ○ c) 90°
   - ○ d) less than 90°

8. An obtuse angle measures _____.
   - ○ a) less than 90°
   - ○ b) 90°
   - ○ c) more than 90°
   - ○ d) 45°

9. A(n) _____ angle measures 90°.
   - ○ a) obtuse
   - ○ b) scalene
   - ○ c) right
   - ○ d) acute

10. An angle is formed by two _____.
   - ○ a) lines
   - ○ b) parallel lines
   - ○ c) line segments
   - ○ d) rays

11. The endpoint R in ∠QRS is also the _____.
   - ○ a) verse
   - ○ b) vernox
   - ○ c) vortex
   - ○ d) vertex

12. This angle's name is _____.

   - ○ a) ∠UTV
   - ○ b) ∠TUV
   - ○ c) ∠UVT
   - ○ d) ∠VT

Unit 6

Practice Test: Geometry (II)

Name_____ Date_____

Fill in the circle next to the correct answer.

1. A triangle with 3 sides of equal length is called _____.
   - ○ a) isosceles
   - ○ b) scalene
   - ○ c) right
   - ○ d) equilateral

2. A triangle with 2 sides of equal length is called _____.
   - ○ a) equilateral
   - ○ b) scalene
   - ○ c) right
   - ○ d) isosceles

3. A triangle with no sides of of equal length is called _____.
   - ○ a) isosceles
   - ○ b) right
   - ○ c) equilateral
   - ○ d) scalene

4. Identify this triangle:
   - ○ a) scalene
   - ○ b) right
   - ○ c) equilateral
   - ○ d) isosceles

5. Identify this triangle:
   - ○ a) right
   - ○ b) scalene
   - ○ c) equilateral
   - ○ d) isosceles

6. An eight-sided polygon is called a(n) _____.
   - ○ a) nonagon
   - ○ b) octagon
   - ○ c) heptagon
   - ○ d) hexagon

7. A decagon has ___ sides.
   - ○ a) 5
   - ○ b) 7
   - ○ c) 10
   - ○ d) 9

8. A quadrilateral has ___ sides.
   - ○ a) 3
   - ○ b) 5
   - ○ c) 2
   - ○ d) 4

9. A 7-sided polygon is called a _____.
   - ○ a) pentagon
   - ○ b) heptagon
   - ○ c) decagon
   - ○ d) hexagon

10. Which letter has a line of symmetry?
    - ○ a) A
    - ○ b) P
    - ○ c) L
    - ○ d) F

11. Congruent figures have the same _____.
    - ○ a) angles and size
    - ○ b) width and shape
    - ○ c) size and height
    - ○ d) size and shape

12. Which letter has a line of symmetry and has congruent opposite sides?
    - ○ a) W
    - ○ b) Q
    - ○ c) G
    - ○ d) J

Answer Key

Page 3

1.

+	0	1	2	3	4	5	6
0	0	1	2	3	4	5	6
1	1	2	3	4	5	6	7
2	3	4	5	6	7	8	9
3	4	5	6	7	8	9	10
4	5	6	7	8	9	10	11
5	6	7	8	9	10	11	12
6	7	8	9	10	11	12	13

2. 4   2   6   5
3. 0   6   0   4
4. 4   7   7   10   9   6   8

Page 4

1. 7   9   6   9
2. 8   6   9   8
3. 8   9   2   5
4. 3   8   5   7
5. 9   7   8   6   7   16   13
6. 9   15   12   3   9   13   14
7. 4   6   14   7   9   12   11
8. 11   15   11   4   17   14   12
9. 8   8   13   7   3   10   18
10. 16   15   11   10   10   8   17

Page 5

1. 4 + 5 = 9
2. 6 + 9 = 15
3. 9 = 3 = 12
4. 7 + 6 = 13
5. 8 + 6 = 14
6. 9 + 9 = 18
7. 7 + 4 = 11
8. 8 + 8 = 16

Page 6

1. 1   9   5   6   1   4   3
2. 6   1   3   5   2   4   1
3. 8   12   10   9   11   12
4. 11   10   12   12   7   3
5. 8   3   0   4   4   3
6. 2   3   3   5   1   4

Page 7

1. 3   7   0   6
2. 1   4   4   3
3. 6   8   9   0
4. 9   1   9   1
5. 1   0   9   1   4   4   5
6. 8   0   2   2   3   1   3
7. 5   4   3   2   8   2   5
8. 1   7   8   4   7   4   6
9. 3   2   7   0   6   7   5
10. 3   6   2   8   1   4   9

Page 8

1. 9 − 4 = 5
2. 12 − 8 = 4
3. 17 − 9 = 8
4. 16 − 9 = 7
5. 12 − 7 = 5
6. 13 − 6 = 7
7. 15 − 6 = 9
8. 14 − 5 = 9

Page 9

1. 9   7   7   6   7   16   13   13
2. 4   10   2   15   8   17   11   16
3. 9   9   11   11   11   9   14   12
4. 15   15   10   8   6   13   11   8
5. 12   2   14   12   10   10   3   18
6. 5   4   3   2   8   2   5   7
7. 6   4   4   9   9   8   8   4
8. 7   5   1   9   0   7   6   7
9. 8   7   6   3   6   9   2   8
10. 5   8   5   9   5   9   9   7

Page 10

1. 9 + 7 = 16 Ⓐ
2. 14 − 6 = 8 Ⓢ
3. 8 + 8 = 16 Ⓐ
4. 9 + 4 = 13 Ⓐ
5. 17 − 8 = 9 Ⓢ
6. 6 + 7 = 13 Ⓐ

Page 11

1. 9, 9 + 6 = 15
2. 6, 6 + 5 = 11
3. 1, 1 + 7 = 8
4. 7, 7 + 9 = 16
5. 3, 3 + 1 = 4
6. 5, 5 + 5 = 10
7. 7, 7 + 3 = 10
9. 9, 9 + 0 = 9
9. 9, 9 + 9 = 18
7. 7, 7 + 6 = 13
9. 9, 9 + 8 = 17
8. 8, 8 + 7 = 15
7. 7, 7 + 2 = 9
3. 3, 3 + 4 = 7
9. 9, 9 + 5 = 14
3. 3, 3 + 8 = 11
8. 8, 8 + 4 = 12
5. 5, 5 + 3 = 8

Page 12

1. 29   88   68   17   55   67
2. 99   78   29   38   19   29
3. 39   47   19   69   16   88
4. 19   59   19   66   19   86
5. 84 + 5 = 89
6. 91 + 5 = 96
7. 20 + 3 = 23

Page 13

1. 39   79   25   18   58   19
2. 66   38   28   18   48   28
3. 96   67   18   29   88   15
4. 57   77   99   87   19   39
5. 4   3   0
6. 3   7   7
7. 22 + 7 = 29

Page 14

1. 24   73   81   13   43   32
2. 11   32   10   21   62   91
3. 40   57   11   21   31   53
4. 3   41   32   65   70   82
5. 68 − 6 = 62
6. 49 − 8 = 41
7. 59 − 7 = 52

Page 15

1. 50   41   65   20   92   80
2. 61   81   93   24   31   11
3. 72   43   12   23   92   25
4. 55   62   70   13   21   82
5. 68   29   17
6. 6   3   5
7. 48 − 7 = 41

Page 16

1. 12   14   13   11   13   11
2. 12   16   11   16   14   11
3. 88   59   14   49   39   67
4. 29   96   85   65   29   17
5. 19   54   77   28   19   99
6. 9   9   9   5   7   7
7. 9   7   9   8   6   9
8. 54   70   34   21   10   42
9. 82   31   91   12   41   82
10. 11   70   42   27   50   91

Page 17

1. b
2. c
3. d
4. a
5. b
6. d
7. c
8. d

Page 18
1. 4, 2   6, 3   3, 7
2. 5, 5   2, 8   7, 4
3. 2, 1   8, 6   1, 9
4. 51 70 42 61 31 82
5. 30 95 22 86 63 35
6. 24 83 34 90 34 83
7. 50 32 92 45 20 55

Page 19
1. 46 30 70 91 22 90
2. 25 72 62 80 51 26
3. 41 50 61 82 20 43
4. 80 91 41 62 84 22
5. 20 64 46 71 97 54
6. 94 45 24 83 25 37
7. 22 98 51 28 65 67

Page 20
1. $62 + 9 = 71$ 4. $46 + 7 = 53$
2. $74 + 8 = 82$ 5. $45 + 6 = 51$
3. $58 + 3 + 5 = 66$ 6. $50 + 7 + 3 = 60$

Page 21
1. 28 18 59 68 47 86
2. 38 13 17 79 28 19
3. 86 19 78 27 69 39
4. 55 48 89 18 73 28
5. 69 37 58 78 49 15
6. 88 19 77 29 68 39
7. 59 48 16 84 27 72
8. 13 24 68 38 55 48

Page 22
1. 41 89 17 79 33 69
2. 59 46 11 69 25 77
3. 38 68 44 55 18 89
4. 27 66 19 46 35 64
5. (NC), 46 (C) (C) (NC), 89
6. (C) (NC), 58 (NC), 38 (NC), 68

Page 23
1. $56 - 7 = 49$
2. $56 - 9 = 47$
3. $22 - 9 = 13$
4. $61 - 2 = 59$
5. $61 - 4 = 57$
6. $22 - 3 = 19$
7. $22 - 9 = 13$

Page 24
1. 60 60 90 50 92 98
2. 55 92 79 98 99 58
3. 97 88 88 58 76 67
4. 87 86 79 39 95 97
5. 57 87 99 59 95 67
6. 48 47 84 68 98 59
7. 29 98 99 89 77 76

Page 25
1. 31 50 51 90 63 91
2. 92 84 91 63 87 95
3. 81 90 93 75 80 81
4. 80 77 83 50 82 76
5. 93 58 94 72 65 36
6. 71 91 71 70 30 70
7. 92 82 87 92 85 83

Page 26
1. 30 50 30 50 75 50
2. 14 24 51 12 25 22
3. 40 26 17 32 33 15
4. 24 22 81 22 42 16
5. 32 26 62 12 66 42
6. 24 12 20 52 12 53
7. 21 35 21 12 53 32

Page 27
1. 39 19 25 45 67 47
2. 18 29 27 47 9 33
3. 46 39 9 19 28 48
4. 56 18 29 15 17 8
5. 8 38 38 16 16 54
6. 17 17 38 67 15 49
7. 42 29 27 7 15 18

Page 28
1. $72 - 64 = 8$ (S)
2. $34 + 42 = 76$ (A)
5. $32 - 14 = 18$ (S)
6. $35 + 45 = 80$ (A)
3. $35 + 42 = 77$ (A)
4. $36 - 12 = 24$ (S)
7. $82 - 54 = 28$ (S)

Page 29
1. 70 100 140 108 103 127
2. 110 111 115 123 112 152
3. 131 135 153 145 100 101
4. 158 160 191 179 158 157
5. 178 195 188 149 176 188
6. 287 229 275 278 382 388

Page 30
1. 399 499 588 675 298 483
2. 768 535 665 779 295 985
3. 499 286 789 569 487 998
4. 160 260 790 571 380 990
5. 477 398 675 596 198 869
6. 397 197 277 199 686 889

Page 31
1. 800 630 765 301 315 995
2. 720 501 312 401 581 205
3. 328 903 785 602 510 823
4. 525 991 358 441 324 471
5. 905 339 507 611 417 502
6. 327 893 222 693 530 288
7. 972 605 428 816 211 564

Page 32
1. 900 619 311 900 711 465
2. 660 360 531 220 723 542
3. 376 840 433 974 961 660
4. $232 + 87 = 319$
5. $510 + 92 = 602$
6. $164 + 48 = 312$

Page 33
1. 330 920 210 340 724 846
2. 514 815 113 311 933 621
3. 811 324 151 640 431 206
4. 333 924 413 713 530 541
5. 250 551 326 611 720 122
6. 212 863 572 372 251 831
7. 444 144 461 514 305 647

Page 34
1. 398 708 919 294 877 553
2. 780 198 373 685 545 267
3. 188 639 395 488 58 808
4. 879 204 267 752 463 185
5. 688 385 72 565 293 478
6. 487 166 648 651 388 722
7. 453 616 256 582 237 358

Page 35
1. 661   176   876   259   513   516
2. 234   69   187   353   268   463
3. 854   168   488   185   51   156
4. 137 – 73 = 64
5. 242 – 93 = 149
6. 702 – 84 = 618
7. 526 – 97 = 429

Page 36
1. c   a   d   2. a   d   b
3. c   a   d   4. c   b   a
5. d   b   d   6. b   a   d

Page 37
1. 2,000   400   80   8   200
2. 3   9,000   80   300   4,000
3. 80   0   3,000   100   9
4. 7,000   100   0   60   5
5. 8   9   6. 2   8
   6   5   6   3
7. 0   2   8. 3   0
   9   8   4   7

Page 38
1. 30,000   300   5   5,000   20
2. 6,000   900   30   10,000   0
3. 20,000   1,000   30   100   50,000
4. 3   5. 6
6. 6   7. 3
8. 8   9. 7
10. 30
11. 30,000
12. 7,000

Page 39
1. 60   80   80   20   40
2. 60   50   40   50   80
3. 30   30   80   70   90
4. 300   800   100   900   500
5. 500   600   200   900   800
6. 400   400   300   700   500
7. 400   450   300   800   530
8. 600   900   770   130   200

Page 40
1.
20	40	80	30
+40	+ 30	+ 70	+ 50
60	**70**	**150**	**80**

2.
700	400	800	100
+ 20	+ 60	+ 50	+ 50
720	**460**	**850**	**150**

3.
60	90	40	40
– 50	– 20	– 20	– 20
10	**70**	**20**	**20**

4.
700	500	700	400
– 90	– 60	– 40	– 10
610	**440**	**660**	**390**

5. 60 + 40 + 20 = 120

Page 41
1. <   <   >   <
2. <   =   <   >
3. >   <   <   >

Answers for question rows 4 and 5 can be any number in the folllowing ranges.
4. 24–27   176–199   1,123–1,221
5. 379–388   5,343–5,366   8,922–8,945
6. 176 > 175 > 67 > 165 > 156
7. 1,222 > 1,212 > 1,211 > 1,121 > 1,112
8. 232 < 233 < 322 < 323 < 333
9. 6,114 < 6,141 < 6,411 < 6,414 < 6,441

Page 42
1. 30; Add 5   7. 18, 27, 36, 45
2. 18; Add 3   8. 21, 18, 15, 12
3. 6; Subtract 6   9. 8, 16, 24, 32, 40
4. 42; Add 7
5. 0; Subtract 4
6. 36; Add 6

Page 43
1. 10, 5, 5 × 2 = 10
2. 7, 7, 7 × 1 = 7
3. 15, 3, 3 × 5 = 15
4. 18, 6, 6 × 3 = 18
5. 16, 2, 2 × 8 = 16
6. 28, 4, 4 × 7 = 28
7. 30, 5, 5 × 6 = 30

Page 44
1. 0   5   9   0   0   1
2. 7   0   6   8   4   0
3. 2   0   5   3   0   0
4. 6   2   0   8   9   0
5. 0   0   0   4   0   0
6. 0   7   0   0   3   0
7. factor   factor   product

Page 45
1. 0, 2, 4, 6, 8, 10, 12, 14, 16, 18
2. 14   6   12   16   2   8
3. 0   3   18   6   7   16
4. 8   2   16   0   8   10
5. 18   14   12   0   10   4
6. 2 × 4 = 8
7. 2 × 7 = 14

Page 46
1. 0, 3, 6, 9, 12, 15, 18, 21, 24, 27
2. 21   9   18   24   3   12
3. 0   0   27   12   7   24
4. 12   3   24   0   8   15
5. 27   21   18   8   15   0
6. 3 × 4 = 12
2. 3 × 8 = 24

Page 47
1. 0, 4, 8, 12, 16, 20, 24, 28, 32, 36
2. 0   7   36   8   12   32
3. 28   16   24   32   4   20
4. 12   28   0   8   20   36
5. 12   4   21   24   8   16
6. 4 × 8 = 32
7. 4 × 9 = 36

Page 48
1. 0, 5, 10, 15, 20, 25, 30, 35, 40, 45
2. 45   35   0   6   0   21
3. 0   3   45   10   15   40
4. 35   20   30   40   5   25
5. 15   5   36   30   10   20
6. 6 × 5 = 30
7. 9 × 5 = 45

Page 49

1.

x	0	1	2	3	4	5	6	7	8	9
0	0	0	0	0	0	0	0	0	0	0
1	0	1	2	3	4	5	6	7	8	9
2	0	2	4	6	8	10	12	14	16	18
3	0	3	6	9	12	15	18	21	24	27
4	0	4	8	12	16	20	24	28	32	36
5	0	5	10	15	20	25	30	35	40	45

2. 5 6 0 9
3. 2 9 5 4
4. 7 2 4 9
5. 1 3 6 3

Page 50

1. 20 21 0 1 9 12
2. 7 0 18 6 4 15
3. 5 6 2 24 0 12
4. 3 14 15 16 18 16
5. 24 28 0 9 1 10
6. 10 2 27 2 21 5
7. 8 18 3 16 4 35
8. 8 12 36 6 24 12
9. 25 7 27 4 0 14
10. 20 6 9 8 8 32

Page 51

1. 5 6 0 8 18 6
2. 3 35 20 27 28 30
3. 10 24 10 12 2 45
4. 18 16 36 1 36 16
5. 5 18 14 15 0 15
6. 21 6 0 4 9 32
7. 4 0 24 24 14 30
8. 32 12 2 28 8 7
9. 12 21 24 27 35 9
10. 12 40 45 16 0 18

Page 52

1. b   2. c
3. a   4. d
5. b   6. d
7. c   8. a

Page 53

1. 387 843 975 896 561 854
2. 998 776 885 778 974 786
3. 973 896 688 498 469 974
4. 888 339 775 968 797 579
5. 916 678 997 948 899 627
6. 858 965 599 996 675 996
7. 488 369 886 756 489 879

Page 54

1. 1,237 1,200 1,611 1,004 1,525 1,031
2. 1,621 1,302 1,243 1,012 1,312 1,401
3. 1,622 1,209 1,103 1,291 1,132 1,011
4. 1,101 1,231 1,213 1,123 1,300 1,433
5. 1,400 1,545 1,260 1,413 1,455 1,603
6. 1,831 1,652 1,003 1,751 1,550 1,140
7. 1,333 1,245 1,301 1,622 1,505 1,611

Page 55

1. c   5. d
2. a   6. b
3. a   7. b
4. b

Page 56

1. 200 300 420 120 410 160
2. 322 512 522 403 264 135
3. 262 211 441 222 435 227
4. 161 321 111 124 335 141
5. 151 136 343 262 511 234
6. 213 125 312 241 220 145
7. 723 232 244 520 472 211

Page 57

1. 306 188 117 226 266 388
2. 138 87 109 367 88 379
3. 178 76 287 359 183 178
4. 181 373 275 79 465 259
5. 226 189 330 373 207 129
6. 144 396 96 297 249 447
7. 289 384 117 123 478 135

Page 58

1. b   5. d
2. d   6. b
3. a   7. a
4. d

Page 59

1. 730 − 679 = 51   Ⓢ
2. 635 + 820 = 1,455   Ⓐ
3. 730 − 354 = 376   Ⓢ
4. 635 − 387 = 248   Ⓢ
6. 452 + 679 = 1,131   Ⓐ
7. 951 − 354 = 597   Ⓢ

Page 60

1. 0, 6, 12, 18, 24, 30, 36, 42, 48, 54
2. 0 42 36 18 30 54
3. 12 12 36 18 6 48
4. 42 35 36 48 12 24
5. 54 6 24 0 25 30
6. 6 x 5 = 30
7. 6 x 3 = 18

Page 61

1. 0, 7, 14, 21, 28, 35, 42, 49, 56, 63
2. 49 21 42 56 7 28
3. 0 20 63 21 14 56
4. 28 7 36 0 18 35
5. 63 14 42 27 35 32
6. 6 x 7 = 42
7. 7 x 9 = 63

Page 62

1. 0, 8, 16, 24, 32, 40, 48, 56, 64, 72
2. 32 8 40 0 24 40
3. 72 16 48 27 56 42
4. 64 24 48 18 8 32
5. 0 63 72 24 16 56
6. 7 x 8 = 56
7. 8 x 4 = 32

Page 63

1. 0, 9, 18, 27, 36, 45, 54, 63, 72, 81
2. 36 9 81 0 49 45
3. 18 56 36 27 18 72
4. 63 27 54 72 9 36
5. 0 63 54 24 45 48
6. 5 x 9 = 45
7. 9 x 8 = 72

Page 64

1. **0** **6** 12 **18** **24** **30** **36** 42 **48** 54
   0 **7** 14 **21** 28 **35** 42 **49** 56 63
   0 8 16 **24** 32 40 **48** **56** **64** **72**
   0 **9** 18 **27** **36** **45** **54** **63** **72** **81**
2. 7 9 9 4
3. 4 8 9 6
4. 7 7 9 8
5. 6 7 9 3
6. 7 7 6 7
7. 8 9 8 6

Page 65

1. 8 14 42 24 18 6
2. 49 48 81 21 14 24
3. 16 9 18 63 32 72
4. 42 45 36 30 0 40
5. 0 30 12 32 54 56
6. 18 9 35 16 27 24
7. 45 0 27 54 28 48
8. 72 12 21 56 64 7
9. 63 24 6 36 35 18
10. 8 40 0 7 28 36

Page 66

1. 8 12 15 24 14 36
2. 15 40 63 48 0 32
3. 24 42 20 12 48 36
4. 18 18 24 10 5 30
5. 9 21 54 8 0 32
6. 21 0 30 7 27 40
7. 18 6 28 27 28 0
8. 0 16 4 20 72 12
9. 0 35 45 56 0 9
10. 2 16 30 3 48 8

Page 67

1. c c c   2. d b c
3. a b a   4. b c c
3. b c a   6. b d a
7. b c a

Page 68

1. 6 x 8 = 48
2. 6 x 9 = 54
3. 5 x 9 = 45
4. 8 x 3 = 24
5. 7 x 8 = 56
6. 6 x 5 = 30
7. 3 x 9 = 27

Page 69

1. 30 33 60 22 10 36
2. 77 90 0 11 44 50
3. 88 70 12 99 40 20
4. 80 55 48 66 24 20
5. 40 60 80 80 90 60
6. 12 x 3 = 36
7. 10 x 9 = 90

Page 70

1. 40 88 39 46 27 60
2. 84 96 86 62 48 88
3. 90 69 28 26 82 60
4. 66 93 63 29 68 44
5. 42 36 69 25 84 64
6. 2 x 21 = 42
7. 2 x 14 = 28

Page 71

1. 60 42 45 92 80 84
2. 91 85 96 38 72 90
3. 72 72 48 84 90 56
4. 54 76 76 96 34 50
5. 64 87 65 78 74 54
6. 51 38 56 70 68 70
7. 36 75 75 96 72 57

Page 72

1. 200 420 240 300 150 140
2. 630 280 320 540 480 450
3. 240 180 720 350 240 300
4. 320 350 210 100 360 560
5. 160 480 560 250 270 160
6. 810 490 360 360 640 200
7. 180 120 540 630 280 240

Page 73

1. 106 328 129 122 148 637
2. 248 204 249 216 205 128
3. 159 648 126 279 126 306
4. 186 244 288 104 164 279
5. 186 166 276 568 186 168
6. 219 549 146 108 567 128
7. 246 279 305 186 819 208

Page 74

1. 140 133 108 144 85 203
2. 224 140 264 207 132 168
3. 112 117 120 100 192 168
4. 148 293 144 135 112 208
5. 136 128 196 216 171 200
6. 108 154 126 165 104 189
7. 288 272 126 225 280 162

Page 75

1. 315 364 264 222 144 558
2. 152 154 177 256 184 178
3. 222 275 336 465 336 392
4. 657 448 340 117 528 413
5. 360 846 406 235 402 696
6. 270 216 255 608 476 468
7. 504 333 276 171 414 592
8. 430 132 318 675 512 686
9. 224 387 348 576 316 201

Page 76

1. 12 x 8 = 96   2. 26 x 4 = 104
3. 68 x 5 = 340   4. 39 x 3 = 117
5. 46 x 9 = 414   6. 35 x 4 = 140
7. 47 x 3 = 141

Page 77

1. 36 56 27 48 54 35
2. 63 32 42 45 32 72
3. 36 50 77 48 66 30
4. 48 99 40 88 40 90
5. 93 84 48 96 88 82
6. 46 66 66 84 86 62
7. 240 720 210 200 720 400
8. 630 140 320 630 540 240
9. 156 128 355 72 168 637

Page 78

1. d a c   4. d d c
2. b c c   5. a d c
3. b c a

Page 79

1. 15 5 3
2. 21 7 3
3. 12 3 4
4. 32 4 8
5. 10 2 5
6. 18 3 6
7. 14 7 2

Page 80
1. 2, 2   2. 4, 4
3. 2, 2   4. 9, 9
5. 5, 5   6. 3, 3
7. 4, 4   8. 4, 4
9. 3, 3   10. 4, 4
11. 4, 4   12. 5, 5

Page 81
1. 0   1   0   1   6   0
2. 0   1   3   0   1   0
3. 1   5   1   0   2   9
4. 8   1   4   0   7   1
5. $6\overline{)6}$ (1)   6. $1\overline{)5}$ (5)

Page 82
1. 1, 1   2, 2   3, 3
2. 4, 4   5, 5   6, 6
3. 7, 7   8, 8   9, 9
4. 1, 1   2, 2   3, 3
5. 4, 4   5, 5   6, 6
6. 7, 7   8, 8   9, 9
7. 4   1   5   8   3   7
8. 4   3   5   8   9   7
9. 9   2   6   2   6   1

Page 83
1. 1, 1   2, 2   3, 3
2. 4, 4   5, 5   6, 6
3. 7, 7   8, 8   9, 9
4. 1, 1   2, 2   3, 3
5. 4, 4   5, 5   6, 6
6. 7, 7   8, 8   9, 9
7. 8   4   2   1   7   3
8. 2   7   9   5   1   3
9. 5   4   6   8   6   9

Page 84
1. 0   1   8   6   6   1
2. 8   9   5   0   4   6
3. 3   3   1   3   9   7
4. 0   4   2   1   3   8
5. 3   0   4   7   5   2
6. 7   5   0   9   4   2
7. 5   3   2   5   2   1
8. 6   9   8   4   6   7
9. 18   36   20   14   15
10. 18   40   2   24   45

Page 85
1. 1, 1   2, 2   3, 3
2. 4, 4   5, 5   6, 6
3. 7, 7   8, 8   9, 9
4. 1, 1   2, 2   3, 3
5. 4, 4   5, 5   6, 6
6. 7, 7   8, 8   9, 9
7. 5   3   5   1   7   7
8. 1   2   6   4   9   8
9. 3   4   6   2   9   8

Page 86
1. 1, 1   2, 2   3, 3
2. 4, 4   5, 5   6, 6
3. 7, 7   8, 8   9, 9
4. 1, 1   2, 2   3, 3
5. 4, 4   5, 5   6, 6
6. 7, 7   8, 8   9, 9
7. 1   9   9   3   5   2
8. 7   8   1   3   7   2
9. 8   4   6   4   6   5

Page 87
1. 9   5   1   5   1   3
2. 4   3   0   9   8   5
3. 1   3   2   7   2   7
4. 9   2   1   2   7   4
5. 0   9   8   6   6   4
6. 8   6   4   7   0   3
7. 8   7   0   6   5   1
8. 36   72   18   49   40
9. 27   48   42   32   54
10. 63   72   24   81   28

Page 88
1. $4\overline{)32}$ (8)   5. $9\overline{)54}$ (6)
2. $4\overline{)28}$ (7)   6. $4\overline{)36}$ (9)
3. $8\overline{)72}$ (9)   7. $7\overline{)42}$ (6)
4. $5\overline{)30}$ (6)

Page 89
1. 6   7   7   3   4   9
2. 9   3   7   2   7   2
3. 4   8   0   2   7   6
4. 6   5   2   3   7   4
5. 9   3   6   9   8   8
6. 5   0   5   7   5   9
7. 4   2   1   8   6   7
8. 2   1   4   8   8   1
9. 6   9   1   3   4   6
10. 0   4   5   5   3   4

Page 90
1. $9\overline{)72}$ (8)   5. $6\overline{)48}$ (8)
2. $8\overline{)24}$ (3)   6. $3\overline{)27}$ (9)
3. $5\overline{)30}$ (6)   7. $4\overline{)36}$ (9)
4. $7\overline{)56}$ (8)

Page 91
1. 42   54   72   14   28   64
2. 12   35   27   56   49   63
3. 12   9   40   48   21   36
4. 25   0   9   24   28   27
5. 3   6   8   6   6   5
6. 4   5   6   9   5   5
7. 5   7   2   8   9   9
8. 5   2   1   8   6   5

Page 92
1. a   c   c   5. a   b   d
2. c   a   b   6. c   b   c
3. b   d   b   7. c   b   d
4. d   c   b
5. a   b   d

Page 93
1. b   5. b
2. d   6. c
3. d   7. d
4. a

Answer Key

Page 94

1. $\frac{1}{2}$ 2. $\frac{1}{4}$
3. $\frac{1}{2}$ 4. $\frac{1}{4}$
5. $\frac{1}{3}$ 6. $\frac{1}{5}$
7. $\frac{1}{3}$ 8. $\frac{1}{6}$
9. $\frac{1}{4}$ 10. $\frac{1}{8}$

Page 95

1. $\frac{1}{4}$ 2. $\frac{3}{8}$
3. $\frac{4}{5}$ 4. $\frac{7}{8}$
5. $\frac{1}{6}$ 6. $\frac{5}{9}$
7. $\frac{5}{6}$ 8. $\frac{7}{9}$
9. $\frac{4}{7}$ 10. $\frac{9}{10}$

Page 96

1. $\frac{1}{2}$ one half 2. $\frac{1}{4}$ one fourth
3. $\frac{1}{3}$ one third 4. $\frac{2}{4}$ two fourths
5. $\frac{2}{3}$ two thirds 6. $\frac{1}{3}$ one third
7. $\frac{1}{2}$ one half 8. $\frac{3}{4}$ three fourths
9. $\frac{2}{4}$ 10. $\frac{1}{3}$

Page 97

1. 5 2 5   2. 5 3 5
3. 6 4 6   4. 8 2 8
5. 9 3 9   6. 9 4 9
7. 7 3 7   8. 4 2 4
9. 3 4 3   10. 6 3 6

Page 98

1. $\frac{4}{5}$ four fifths 2. $\frac{5}{6}$ five sixths
3. $\frac{2}{6}$ two sixths 4. $\frac{4}{7}$ four sevenths
5. $\frac{1}{7}$ one seventh 6. $\frac{3}{5}$ three fifths
7. $\frac{4}{5}$ four fifths 8. $\frac{6}{7}$ six sevenths
9. $\frac{3}{7}$ 10. $\frac{3}{5}$

Page 99

1. $\frac{1}{8}$ one eighth 2. $\frac{2}{9}$ two ninths
3. $\frac{4}{9}$ four ninths 4. $\frac{7}{10}$ seven tenths
5. $\frac{1}{10}$ one tenth 6. $\frac{5}{9}$ five ninths
7. $\frac{3}{8}$ three eighths 8. $\frac{9}{10}$ nine tenths
9. $\frac{3}{8}$ 10. $\frac{7}{10}$

Page 100

1. 9 9 9   2. 9 8 9
3. 7 7 7   4. 3 6 3
5. 7 6 7   6. 4 5 4
7. 5 9 5   8. 9 6 9
9. 9 7 9   10. 8 7 8

Page 101

1. c   2. b
3. c   4. a
5. d   6. b
7. d

Page 102

1. $3.15   2. $4.20
3. $5.52   4. $10.65
5. $2.12   6. $15.00
7. $7.10   8. $20.30
9. $12.11   10. $42.40
11. $16.50 12. $60.55
13. $1.63   14. $6.99
15. $11.90 16. $90.18

Page 103

1. $0.32   7. $0.70
2. $0.75   8. $2.40
3. $0.81   9. $4.01
4. $0.90   10. $5.60
5. $0.29   11. $10.10
6. $0.53   12. $1.09

Page 104

1. $1.45 $4.65 $6.19 $9.97 $7.98
2. $8.66 $7.64 $6.30 $3.03 $6.10
3. $9.12 $8.84 $8.88 $8.05 $11.14
4. $2.15 $6.36 $9.40 $2.20 $5.62
5. $3.41 $6.35 $8.56 $1.09 $2.51
6. $3.07 $1.89 $0.81 $1.20 $1.66

Page 105

1. $1.98 + .89¢ = $2.87 (A)
2. $5.00 − $3.98 = $1.02 (S)
3. $6.42 − .75¢ = $5.67 (S)
4. $9.45 − $7.20 = $2.25 (S)
5. $1.79 + $2.95 = $4.74 (A)
6. $2.25 − $1.59 = .66¢ (S)
7. $4.00 + $2.39 = $6.39 (A)

Page 106

1. b   4. d
2. c   5. a
3. a   6. c

Page 107
1. 3 in.
2. $2\frac{1}{2}$ in.
3. $1\frac{3}{4}$ in.
4. $4\frac{1}{4}$ in.
5. $3\frac{1}{4}$ in.

Use a ruler to check accuracy for questions 6-10.

Page 108
1. 1 ft.	1 yd.	2 ft.
2. 3 ft.	6 ft.	5 yd.
3. 12 ft.	108 in.	10 yd.
4. 84 in.	15 yd.	144 in.
5. 144 in.	60 ft.	150 ft.
6. 60 in.
7. 36 ft.
8. 72 in.
9. 8 yd.
10. 3 yd.

Page 109
1. lb.
2. oz.
3. oz.
4. lb.
5. lb.
6. oz.
7. lb.
8. oz.
9. 16 oz.
10. 32 oz.
11. 24 oz.
12. 2,000 lb.
13. 1,000 lb.
14. 4 lb.
15. 2 lb.
16. 160 oz.
17. 10,000 lb.
18. 96 oz.
19. 56 oz.
20. 2 T.

Page 110
1. gallons
2. cups
3. cups
4. pints
5. cups
6. quarts
7. 1 pint
8. 2 quarts
9. 2 gallons
10. 16 oz.
11. 64 oz.
12. 3 pints
13. 256 oz.
14. 5 quarts
15. 96 oz.
16. 4 gallons
17. 32 oz.
18. 128 oz.
19. 16 cups
20. 6 gallons
21. 160 oz.
22. 4 gallons

Page. 111
1. b
2. a
3. d
4. b
5. c
6. a
7. d
8. a
9. d
10. d
11. c
12. d

Page 112
1. h
2. g
3. f
4. i
5. j
6. e
7. c
8. k
9. a
10. l
11. b
12. d
13. s
14. r
15. p
16. m
17. v
18. n
19. u
20. x
21. q
22. o
23. t
24. w

Page 113
1. 3 cm.
2. 5 cm.
3. 9 cm.
4. 12 cm.

Use a ruler to check accuracy for questions 5-11.

11. 2 in. = about <u>5</u> cm.

Page 114
Use a ruler to check accuracy for questions 1-3.

4. 1 m.
5. 1 km.
6. 5 m.
7. 7 km.
8. 10 m.
9. 10 km.
10. 100 km.
11. 20,000 m.
12. 40,000 m.
13. 65,000 m.
14. 10 cm.
15. 3 in.
16. 15 cm.
17. 9 in.
18. 30 cm.
19. 11 in.
20. 90 cm.; 1 m.

Page 115
1. g.
2. kg.
3. kg.
4. g.
5. kg.
6. g.
7. kg.
8. kg.
9. g.
10. g.
11. 1 kg.
12. 10 kg.
13. 5 kg
14. 25 kg.
15. an ounce of sugar
16. a kilogram of salt
17. 2,000 kilograms

Page 116
1. ml.
2. liter
3. liter
4. ml.
5. liter
6. liter
7. ml.
8. ml.
9. 1 liter
10. 5 liters
11. 10 liters
12. 4,000 ml.
13. 12,000 ml.
14. 60 ml.
15. 240 ml.
16. 1 liter
17. 2 liters
18. 4 liters
19. the liter bottles
20. a 4-liter container

Page 117
1. b
2. c
3. c
4. d
5. b
6. c
7. a
8. a
9. b
10. a
11. d
12. c

Page 118
1. 48 in.
2. 2,000 cm.
3. 3,000 kg.
4. 12 cups
5. 3 oz.
6. 81 feet
7. milliliters
8. 23 cm.
9. 4 oz.
10. 48 pints
11. 80 oz.
12. a kilogram of tea

Use a ruler to check accuracy for questions 13 and 14.

Page 119
1. 28   31   30
2. Monday
3. Friday
4. Tuesday
5. 5
6. 4
7. March 15
8. April 3
9. 7
10. 14
11. 42
12. 84

Page 120
1. 7   31 x 7 = 217
2. 4   30 x 4 = 120
3. 217 + 120 = 337   337 + 28 = 365
4. every 4 years
5. February 29th
6. 2008, 2012
7. F   8. F
9. F   10. T
11. T   12. F

Page 121
1. 120   300   4:20
2. 510   570   6:00
3. 2:15   3:30   1:20   9:52
4. 5:40   7:10   12:12   6:47
5. 8:14   10:36   11:48   4:16

Page 122
1. 48   120   168
2. 3:30a.m. 5:40a.m. 8:25a.m. 4:52a.m.
3. 4:02p.m. 12:05p.m. 6:45p.m. 7:28p.m.
Answers will vary for question rows 4 and 5.

Page 123
1. 65 min.   2. 111 min.
   1 hr., 5 min.   1 hr., 51 min.
3. 98 min.   4. 107 min.
   1 hr., 38 min.   1 hr., 47 min.
5. 168 min.   6. 168 min.
   2 hrs., 48 min.   2 hrs., 48 min.
7. 106 min.   8. 177 min.
   1 hr., 46 min.   2 hrs., 57 min.
9. 221 min.   10. 219 min.
   3 hrs., 41 min.   3 hrs., 39 min.

Page 124
1. Thursday
2. Tuesday
3. 5
4. 14th   26th
5. 13th   8th
6. September, April, November
7. 365   366
8. 21   49   63
9. 24   96   144
10. 8:00 a.m.   8:00 p.m.
11. 2:37
12. 3:00
13. 23
14. 42 minutes

Page 125
1. c   7. c
2. b   8. a
3. d   9. d
4. d   10. a
5. d   11. d
6. a

Page 126
Use a ruler to check accuracy for questions 1-4.

5. 2 ft.   6. 48 hours
7. 1 yd.   8. 365 days
9. 2 pints   10. 25,000 m.
11. 3 gallons   12. 2,000 g.
13. 2 m.   14. 4 lb.
15. 3 km.   16. 5 hours
17. 10 kg.   18. 63 days
19. 3 T.   20. 192 hours
21. 31   28   31   30
22. 31   30   31   31
23. 30   31   30   31

Page 127
1. d   7. d
2. b   8. a
3. a   9. b
4. c   10. b
5. d   11. a
6. b   12. c

Page 128
1. 3   5   7   10
2. 4   9   20   12
3. 30   25   14   17
4. 19   26   24   29
5. 33   32   49   38
6. II   IV   V   IX
7. X   XV   XX   XXIII
8. XVI   XIX   XXVII   XXX
9. XXIV   XXIX   XXXV   XXXVIII
10. XXXX   XXXXIV   XXXIX   XXXXVI

Page 129
1. Troop B   Troop A
2. Troop C
3. Troop A
4. 10
5. 15
6. *Have teacher or parent check bar graph for accuracy.*

Page 130
1. Week 2   Week 4
2. 15
3. increase
4. decrease
5. Week 4
6. *Have teacher or parent check line graph for accuracy.*

Page 131
1. $\overrightarrow{QR}$ $\overline{UV}$
2. $\overleftrightarrow{MN}$ $\overrightarrow{YZ}$
3. $\overleftrightarrow{EF}//\overleftrightarrow{GH}$
4. $\overleftrightarrow{IJ}\perp\overleftrightarrow{KL}$ $\overleftrightarrow{ST}$
5. $\overline{OP}$ $\overrightarrow{WX}$

Have teacher or parent check lines 6-8 for accuracy.

Answer Key

Page 132
1. ∠DEF   ∠QRS or ∠SRQ
2. ∠XYZ or ∠ZYX   ∠LMN or ∠NML
3. acute   right   obtuse
4. right   obtuse   right
5. acute   acute   obtuse
6. acute
7. right
8. obtuse

Page 133
1. scalene   isosceles   equilateral
2. isosceles   scalene   scalene
3. equilateral   isosceles   isosceles
4. scalene   equilateral   scalene
5. equilateral   scalene   isosceles
6. scalene
7. isosceles
8. equilateral

Page 134
1. octagon
2. triangle
3. 5
4. 10
5. quadrilateral
6. heptagon   octagon   quadrilateral
7. pentagon   nonagon   hexagon
8. triangle   quadrilateral   decagon

Page 135
1. (hexagon)
2. 0
3. I
4. *Have teacher or parent to check accuracy.*
5. a, d
6. b, d
7. a, c
8. yes

Page 136
1. 16 in.
2. 24 cm.
3. 6 yd.
4. 50 mm.
5. 32 ft.
6. 90 cm.
7. 24 yd.
8. 12 km.
9. 80 yd.

Page 137
1. a
2. c
3. b
4. c
5. a
6. b
7. a
8. b
9. c
10. c
11. c
12. b

Page 138
1. b
2. d
3. a
4. b
5. c
6. b
7. c
8. c
9. a
10. b
11. c

Page 139
1. b
2. b
3. b
4. a
5. d
6. a
7. c
8. b
9. a
10. c
11. c
12. b

Page 140
1. b
2. c
3. d
4. a
5. d
6. b
7. a
8. b
9. c
10. d
11. b
12. a

Page 141
1. b
2. b
3. c
4. d
5. b
6. c
7. d
8. c
9. a
10. d
11. b
12. b

Page 142
1. c
2. d
3. b
4. c
5. b
6. a
7. c
8. b
9. a
10. a
11. d
12. a

Page 143
1. d
2. b
3. a
4. b
5. c
6. b
7. a
8. b
9. c
10. a
11. a
12. b

Page 144
1. c
2. c
3. c
4. b
5. c
6. d
7. b
8. d
9. b
10. d
11. a
12. d

Page 145
1. a
2. d
3. d
4. b
5. a
6. b
7. d
8. b
9. d
10. c
11. b
12. c

Page 146
1. d
2. c
3. a
4. c
5. d
6. a
7. c
8. d
9. b
10. a
11. b
12. c

Page 147
1. b
2. d
3. d
4. b
5. b
6. d
7. a
8. b
9. a
10. d
11. b
12. b

Page 148
1. a
2. c
3. d
4. d
5. c
6. d
7. a
8. d
9. c
10. b

Page 149
1. d
2. d
3. b
4. a
5. d
6. c
7. d
8. c
9. c
10. d
11. d
12. b

Page 150
1. d
2. d
3. d
4. a
5. d
6. b
7. c
8. d
9. b
10. a
11. d
12. a